The Open University

Practical modern
statistics

Book 2

Time series

About this course

M249 Practical Modern Statistics uses the software packages *SPSS for Windows* (SPSS Inc.) and *WinBUGS*, and other software. This software is provided as part of the course, and its use is covered in the *Introduction to statistical modelling* and in the four computer books associated with *Books 1* to *4*.

Cover image courtesy of NASA. This photograph, acquired by the ASTER instrument on NASA's Terra satellite, shows an aerial view of a large alluvial fan between the Kunlun and Altun mountains in China's Xinjiang province. For more information, see NASA's Earth Observatory website at http://earthobservatory.nasa.gov.

This publication forms part of an Open University course. Details of this and other Open University courses can be obtained from the Student Registration and Enquiry Service, The Open University, PO Box 197, Milton Keynes, MK7 6BJ, United Kingdom: tel. +44 (0)870 333 4340, e-mail general-enquiries@open.ac.uk

Alternatively, you may visit the Open University website at http://www.open.ac.uk where you can learn more about the wide range of courses and packs offered at all levels by The Open University.

To purchase a selection of Open University course materials, visit the webshop at www.ouw.co.uk, or contact Open University Worldwide, Michael Young Building, Walton Hall, Milton Keynes, MK7 6AA, United Kingdom, for a brochure: tel. +44 (0)1908 858785, fax +44 (0)1908 858787, e-mail ouwenq@open.ac.uk

The Open University, Walton Hall, Milton Keynes, MK7 6AA.

First published 2007.

Edited, designed and typeset by The Open University, using the Open University TEX System.

Printed in the United Kingdom by Hobbs the Printers Ltd, Totton, SO40 3WX.

ISBN 978 0 7492 1367 1

1.1

Contents

Study guide

You should schedule eighteen study sessions for this book. This includes time for working through *Computer Book 2*, answering the TMA questions and consolidating your work on *Book 2*. You should schedule six study sessions for each of Parts I, II and III.

The sections vary in length. In Part I, Section 1 is shorter than average, and Section 4 is longer than average. In Part II, Sections 6 and 7 are both a little shorter than average, and Section 9 is longer than average. In Part III, Sections 12 and 14 are a little longer than average, and Section 13 is shorter than average.

As you study this book you will be asked to work through *Computer Book 2*. We recommend that you work through the chapters at the points indicated in the text. Your work on each part of the book will include two computer sessions. However, if you wish, you can postpone the first computer session in each part of the book and study it with the second at the end of your study of that part.

A possible study pattern is as follows.

Part I

Study session 1: Section 1.
Study session 2: Section 2.
Study session 3: Section 3. You will need access to your computer for this session.
Study session 4: Section 4.
Study session 5: Section 5. You will need access to your computer for this session.
Study session 6: TMA questions on Part I.

Part II

Study session 7: Section 6.
Study session 8: Section 7.
Study session 9: Section 8. You will need access to your computer for this session.
Study session 10: Subsections 9.1 and 9.2.
Study session 11: Subsection 9.3 and Section 10. You will need access to your computer for this session.
Study session 12: TMA questions on Part II.

Part III

Study session 13: Section 11. You will need access to your computer for this session.
Study session 14: Section 12.
Study session 15: Section 13.
Study session 16: Section 14.
Study session 17: Section 15. You will need access to your computer for this session.
Study session 18: TMA questions on Part III and consolidation of your work on this book.

Introduction

A time series is a sequence of observations made over time. Data of this type are probably among the most commonly encountered: open any magazine or newspaper, watch any television news programme, and you are likely to be presented with a graph showing a time series — of house prices, performance indicators of one kind or another, share indices, or changes in voters' intentions. Many automatic monitoring devices generate time series data in vast quantities, from air quality monitors to seismometers (which measure movements in the Earth's crust). The availability of time series data has been greatly enhanced by the publication of official statistics on the internet.

Some of the main modern statistical methods for analysing time series data are introduced in this book. There are three main reasons why special methods for analysing such data are required. First, temporal patterns — that is, patterns occurring over time, such as trends and seasonal variation — are often of interest, and special methods are needed to display and analyse these patterns. Some of these methods are discussed in Part I. Secondly, forecasts of future values of a time series are often required. Some commonly used forecasting methods are discussed in Part II. A third, more technical reason why special methods are needed is that observations taken at different time points cannot usually be assumed to be independent; for example, the ambient temperatures in a given location on successive days are likely to be positively correlated. Many standard statistical methods, including those that you have met so far in this course, apply only to independent observations, and a different approach is required to cope with correlated observations. A flexible modelling framework for this purpose is discussed in Part III.

Time series are among the earliest data to have been collected in a systematic fashion. Nevertheless, statistical methods for the analysis of time series data were only formalized in the second half of the twentieth century. Today, time series modelling is a major area of statistics, which makes use of much elegant (and sometimes rather difficult) mathematics. In keeping with the aims of this course, this book will avoid the technicalities. Instead, it will concentrate on important concepts, with an emphasis on practical modelling using the statistical package SPSS.

Part I   Decomposition models

Introduction to Part I

Time series data can be characterized by different components, each of which may represent a feature of particular interest. In some situations, the main issue of interest is whether the data show a general upward or downward trend. In others, it is the variation within an annual cycle that is most relevant. Occasionally, the variation that remains after trends and seasonal fluctuations have been accounted for is the primary focus of an analysis.

In Part I, you will learn how to identify, display, combine and estimate the components of a time series. In Section 1, time series are defined, and their typical features are described and illustrated with practical examples. In Section 2, a modelling framework for time series is introduced, and methods for choosing an appropriate model are described. In Section 3, you will learn how to use SPSS to enter, display and transform time series data. Methods for estimating the components of a time series are described in Section 4. Finally, in Section 5, you will learn how to use SPSS to analyse time series data using this component-based approach.

1   Time series and their components

In this section, time series are introduced and their features are described. In Subsection 1.1, graphical methods for displaying time series data are presented. In Subsection 1.2, the components of a time series are defined, and graphical methods are used to describe these components.

1.1   Presenting time series data

In its most general form, a time series is a collection of observations X_t on some random variable X at different times $t = t_1, t_2, \ldots$. Activity 1.1 provides an example of a typical time series.

Activity 1.1   Visits overseas by UK residents

The Office for National Statistics publishes a monthly series of the number of visits overseas by UK residents. The data are derived from the International Passenger Survey (IPS), a sample survey of around 250 000 interviews carried out per year.

The data collected for each month from January 1980 to December 2004 are presented in Table 1.1. Each entry in the table is the number of thousands of visits overseas by UK residents during a particular month and year. The month is specified in the row at the top of the table, and the year is given in the column on the left-hand side of the table.

These data were obtained in July 2005 from the National Statistics website http://www.statistics.gov.uk.

Crown copyright material is reproduced with the permission of the Controller of HMSO.

Table 1.1   Monthly series of number of visits overseas by UK residents (thousands)

	Jan	Feb	Mar	Apr	May	Jun	Jul	Aug	Sep	Oct	Nov	Dec
1980	823	780	1058	1397	1438	1821	1950	2777	2258	1509	1004	690
1981	833	818	1067	1521	1559	1828	2177	3143	2547	1812	1006	737
1982	962	872	1106	1671	1524	2261	2247	3268	2741	2018	1087	854
1983	947	875	1156	1616	1646	2142	2677	3187	2711	2027	1098	912
1984	1035	885	1336	1717	1828	2436	2480	3150	2968	2054	1235	950
1985	1043	872	1365	1644	1651	2288	2277	3150	2830	2050	1424	1014
1986	1129	1004	1572	1607	2116	2620	2865	3740	3318	2457	1465	1055
1987	1305	1292	1644	2074	2391	2849	3148	4041	3462	2540	1603	1098
1988	1406	1384	1679	2080	2133	3130	3326	3967	3729	3077	1695	1224
1989	1724	1627	2055	2211	2478	3263	3353	4392	3878	3006	1647	1398
1990	1808	1532	1925	2535	2468	3216	3392	4285	3799	3091	1884	1215
1991	1695	1429	2024	2703	2317	2896	3323	4301	3734	3072	1929	1386
1992	1879	1800	2391	2912	2993	3098	3645	4479	3937	3146	2075	1477
1993	2046	1995	2572	2762	2968	3692	3845	4825	4215	3793	2240	1767
1994	2035	2117	2618	2994	3329	4119	4161	5113	4620	4037	2388	2100
1995	2267	2207	2711	3360	3486	4147	4356	5055	4617	4241	2537	2362
1996	2253	2314	2965	3325	3299	4118	4142	5178	4569	4405	2975	2508
1997	2541	2582	3030	3359	3911	4619	4580	5736	4865	4556	3459	2719
1998	2817	3035	3327	3818	4604	4820	5139	6188	5648	4910	3661	2906
1999	3183	3052	3644	4244	4605	5726	5391	6525	5821	5423	3465	2802
2000	3020	3340	3782	4568	4693	5532	5931	7031	6275	5706	3747	3213
2001	3533	3362	3947	4995	4589	6077	5982	7472	6198	5271	3919	2935
2002	3326	3503	4114	4848	4695	6068	5877	7520	6332	5827	3908	3359
2003	3564	3663	4279	4830	5401	6066	6219	7855	6256	5717	4080	3494
2004	3878	3986	4020	5244	5075	6573	6357	8142	6704	6205	4260	3693

(a) Look down the columns of Table 1.1. Comment briefly on the variation from year to year.

(b) Now look across the rows. Identify the peak months for visits overseas by UK residents.

In this course, time series in which the observations X_t are made at equally-spaced time intervals are considered. These time points may be labelled $1, 2, 3, \ldots, t, t+1, \ldots$. It will also be assumed that X_t is continuous, or that it can be treated as if it were continuous (as is the case in Activity 1.1).

Time series data in tabular form can be used to identify the presence of marked trends over time and clear seasonal effects, as illustrated in Activity 1.1. However, it is much more difficult to identify subtle features, such as the broad shape of the trend, and the magnitude of the seasonal variation. For this reason, time series data are usually presented graphically rather than in tabular form. The most natural plot is the **time plot**, in which the observed values x_t are plotted against time t.

Example 1.1   *Time plot of visits overseas by UK residents*

The time plot for the data in Table 1.1 is shown in Figure 1.1.

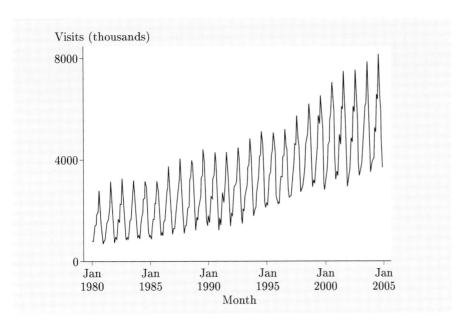

Figure 1.1   Monthly visits overseas by UK residents

To obtain this plot, the data in Table 1.1 have been reorganized into two columns:
a column of time points (successive months between January 1980 and
December 2004) and a column of observations on the numbers of visits. Notice
that, even though the observations correspond to discrete time points (in this
case, months), successive points are joined by straight lines. This enhances the
display by creating an impression of change over time. The upward trend and the
seasonal variation that you identified in Activity 1.1 are immediately apparent:
the presence of an increasing trend is indicated by the overall upward drift in the
time series; the seasonal variation produces the regular fluctuations that give the
plot its sawtoothed appearance.   ◆

Activity 1.2   *Interpreting time plots*

Some further features of the data revealed by the time plot in Figure 1.1 are
considered in this activity.

Use the time plot to answer the following questions.

(a) In your opinion, is the trend from year to year linear (that is, straight), or
curved?

(b) The extent of the seasonal variation can be measured by the size of the
fluctuations, that is, by the difference between the maximum value and the
minimum value within each year. In your opinion, is the size of these
fluctuations constant, or does it vary over time?

Graphical methods play an important role in time series analysis, perhaps even more so than in other areas of statistics. Nevertheless, they have limitations. In particular, it is not always easy to identify trends and seasonality, or other features, from a time plot. This is illustrated in Example 1.2.

Example 1.2   Central England temperatures, 1659–2004

The time series of Central England temperatures gives monthly average surface air temperatures expressed in degrees Celsius (°C) for a region representative of the English Midlands. This time series is remarkable in that it dates back to 1659. The series is routinely updated by the Meteorological Office's Hadley Centre for Climate Prediction and Research.

These data were obtained from the Met Office website http://www.met-office.gov.uk in February 2005.

For each year, the annual average temperature is obtained by calculating the mean of the twelve monthly values of the original series. A time plot of the annual average temperatures is shown in Figure 1.2.

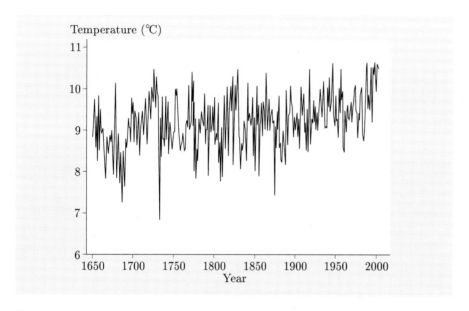

Figure 1.2   Annual average temperatures (°C), 1659–2004

Since the observations are annual averages, there is no seasonality in this series. However, it is of interest to examine whether there are any long-term trends, or whether there are any other patterns, such as cycles of years with high and low average temperatures.

There is considerable variability from year to year. The annual average temperatures in the late seventeenth century were perhaps lower than at subsequent times. However, overall there is no obvious pattern. In particular, it is not clear whether or not there is an upward trend. In this instance, a visual examination of the time plot yields little definite information about long-term trends or other patterns such as cyclic variation.   ◆

Example 1.2 shows that methods other than graphs may be needed to reveal the underlying features of a time series. Much of this book is devoted to presenting appropriate tools with which to reveal such features. Nevertheless, examining a time plot is an essential first step in analysing a time series. Activity 1.3 will give you some practice at doing this.

Activity 1.3 Beer consumption

Figure 1.3 shows the time plot of quarterly beer consumption in the UK, measured in thousands of hectolitres, between the first quarter (January to March) of 1991 and the second quarter (April to June) of 2004.

A hectolitre is one hundred litres.

These data are based on data obtained from the website http://www.bized.ac.uk/timeweb in February 2005.

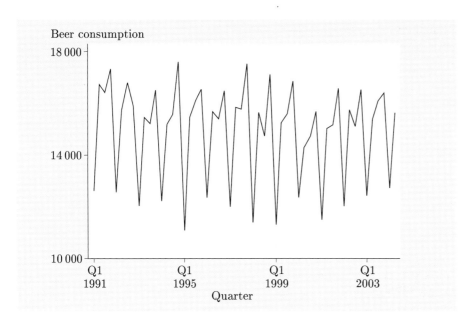

Figure 1.3 Quarterly beer consumption (in thousands of hectolitres), 1991–2004

Comment briefly on any patterns you notice in this time series.

1.2 Components of time series

In Subsection 1.1, time series were described informally in terms of trends, seasonality and cycles. These terms are defined more precisely in this subsection.

A **cycle** is a regular pattern that repeats at fixed intervals. The time interval from the beginning of one cycle to the beginning of the next cycle is called the **period** of the cycle. A cycle whose period is known to be determined by the natural clock (for example, repeating day after day, or year after year) is said to be **seasonal**.

A seasonal cycle with period one year is said to be **annual**. For example, temperatures and other weather indicators, such as precipitation (which includes rain, sleet, snow and hail) or daily sunshine hours, display annual seasonality. Many social and economic time series, such as energy consumption levels and travel, also display annual seasonality, as do medical time series such as numbers of colds and numbers of deaths.

In this book, most of the cycles considered are annual seasonal cycles, but it is important to remember that not all cycles are seasonal and not all seasonality is annual. An example of a seasonal cycle that is not annual is the circadian cycle, which affects many biological processes such as body temperature; this has a period of 24 hours. There are many examples of time series with non-seasonal cycles. For instance, cases of many infectious diseases occur in regular cycles (known as epidemic cycles) of period longer than one year. Before vaccination was

Some authors also use the term cycle to describe long-term fluctuations that repeat at intervals of varying length. In M249 all cycles have a fixed period.

11

introduced, the weekly counts of numbers of cases of measles and whooping cough in the UK followed cycles with periods of two years and four years, respectively, so these cycles are not seasonal. Sunspot activity provides another example of a time series with a non-seasonal cycle. Sunspot activity follows a cycle of period between ten and eleven years.

Sunspots are dark patches that occur on the Sun.

Another example of a time series with a non-seasonal cycle is given in Activity 1.4.

Activity 1.4   *Blood pressure*

The blood pressure (in mm Hg) of an individual was measured at intervals of two milliseconds over a period of two seconds. The time plot of blood pressure measurements is shown in Figure 1.4.

These data were obtained in January 2004 from the website of the European Society for Hypertension Working Group on Blood Pressure and Heart Rate Variability http://www.cbi.dongnocchi.it/glossary.

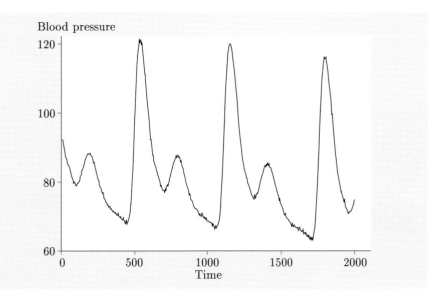

Figure 1.4   Blood pressure (in mm Hg) over time (milliseconds)

(a) How many complete cycles do you observe? Briefly describe the shape of each cycle.

(b) The period of a cycle can be estimated roughly by calculating the average time between successive peaks. Use the location of the high peaks in Figure 1.4 to estimate the period of the cycle.

For the blood pressure data in Figure 1.4, the shape of the cyclical variation (for example, when the highs and lows occur) is easy to describe. This is not always the case. A different type of plot, called a **seasonal plot**, is often useful for displaying seasonality. In a seasonal plot for annual seasonality, a separate line is drawn for each year: for each year, the values x_t of the time series are plotted against the time of year. This is illustrated in Example 1.3.

Example 1.3   Seasonal plots

The time plot in Figure 1.1 for the time series of visits overseas is reproduced in Figure 1.5(a).

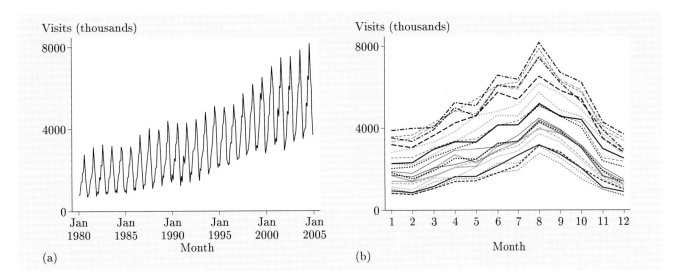

Figure 1.5   Monthly visits overseas: (a) time plot (b) seasonal plot

The time series clearly has a regular pattern. However, it is not easy to describe this pattern from the time plot as the cycles are squashed together. A seasonal plot can help in this situation.

The seasonal plot in Figure 1.5(b) shows the data for each year as a separate line. Owing to the upward trend in the data, the lines for later years tend to lie above those for earlier years, thus producing the layered effect in the diagram. However, all the lines have roughly the same shape, indicating that there is seasonal variation of period one year. The numbers of visits overseas are highest in the summer months, and lowest in the winter months.   ◆

If a time series fluctuates around some fixed value, it is said to have a constant mean value or constant **level**. A time series is said to display a **trend** if there is a gradual change in the mean value or level of the series. Note the word 'gradual' here: short-term fluctuations or cycles with short periods do not represent trends. However, there is a potential difficulty with what is meant by 'short-term': how short is 'short-term'? It is difficult to be precise about this. In this book, 'short-term' is taken to mean short *in relation to the length of the data series*. The distinction between cycles and trend is illustrated in Figure 1.6 (overleaf).

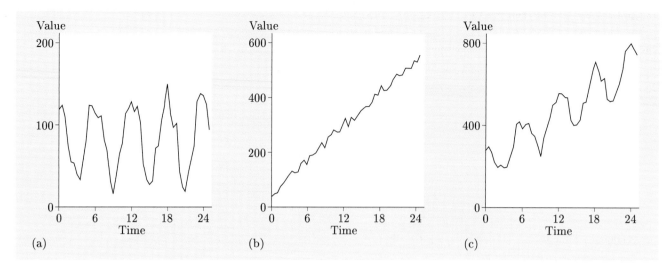

Figure 1.6   Trends and cycles

The time series in Figure 1.6(a) has a cycle but no trend, so it has a constant level: the time series repeats (with random variation) in successive periods. The time series in Figure 1.6(b) shows a trend, in this case an increasing one, but no cycle. Figure 1.6(c) shows a time series with both a cycle and a trend: the cyclical pattern repeats in successive periods, but at different levels.

In addition to trends and cycles, time series also display apparently random fluctuations. These constitute the **irregular** component of the time series. The irregular component is the main feature of the time plot of annual average temperatures in Central England shown in Figure 1.2.

The various components of a time series are illustrated in Example 1.4.

Example 1.4   *Monthly average house prices in the UK, 1991–2005*

Figure 1.7 shows the time series of monthly average house prices in the UK (in pounds sterling) between January 1991 and January 2005.

These data were obtained in February 2005 from the website of the Nationwide Building Society www.nationwide.co.uk/hpi.

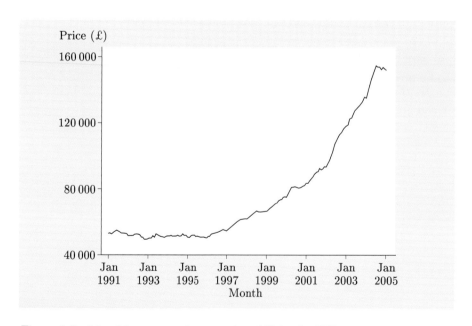

Figure 1.7   Monthly average house prices (£) in the UK

The dominant feature of this time series is the upward trend after 1996, which continued until at least the middle of 2004. Prior to 1996, house prices appear stable. However, the trend since 1996 is so dominant that it obscures other features of the time series.

Figure 1.8(a) shows the time plot for the first five years, January 1991 to December 1995, before the steep upward trend began.

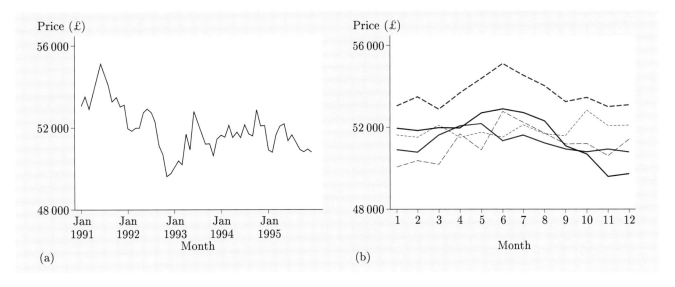

Figure 1.8   Monthly average UK house prices, 1991–95: (a) time plot (b) seasonal plot

Much more detail is visible in Figure 1.8(a) than in the time plot for the entire series in Figure 1.7: the scale on the vertical axis has changed, and as a result, small irregularities in Figure 1.7 appear as big peaks and troughs in Figure 1.8(a). The irregular component of the series is more apparent than it was in Figure 1.7, with clear month-to-month variation in prices.

The seasonal plot for the first five years, which is shown in Figure 1.8(b), suggests that there is some seasonal variation: house prices tend to peak in May and June each year. However, the seasonal variation is not very marked, and appears to be absent in some years.

The features evident from Figures 1.7 and 1.8 may be summarized as follows. The time series of UK house prices between 1991 and 2005 displays trend, seasonal and irregular components. The seasonal component is rather weak. The dominant component is a steep upward trend after 1996: house prices roughly trebled between 1996 and 2005.   ◆

Summary of Section 1

In this section, you have met several examples of time series. Graphical methods for presenting time series data have been presented, and the interpretation of time plots and seasonal plots has been discussed. The main components of time series have been defined, including trend, cyclic and irregular components.

Exercises on Section 1

Exercise 1.1   Central England temperatures, 1951–2004

The time plot for the time series of annual average temperatures in Central England from 1659 to 2004 was shown in Figure 1.2. Figure 1.9 shows the data for the last 54 years, that is, for 1951 to 2004.

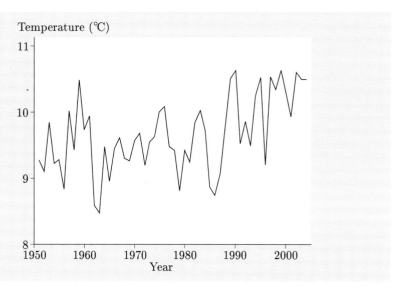

Figure 1.9   Annual average temperatures (°C) in Central England, 1951–2004

(a) Explain why this time series has no seasonal component.

(b) Briefly describe the trend component in this time series, and estimate the overall change in the annual average temperature over the 54-year period.

(c) How important is the irregular component in this time series? Comment briefly on the extent of apparently random year-to-year variation in annual average temperatures, and on the impact that this has on visualizing the trend.

Exercise 1.2   Seasonality of beer consumption

A seasonal plot of the quarterly beer consumption data described in Activity 1.3 is shown in Figure 1.10.

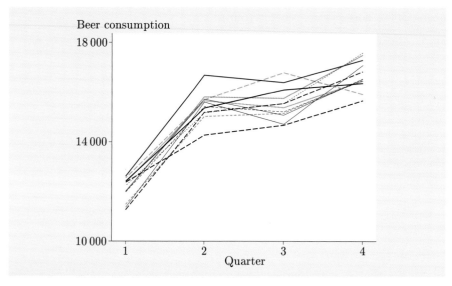

Figure 1.10   Seasonal plot of quarterly beer consumption (thousands of hectolitres)

Is beer consumption in the UK seasonal? If you think it is seasonal, describe the seasonal variation.

2 A modelling framework for time series

In Section 1, three components of time series were introduced: the trend component, the seasonal (or cyclic) component, and the irregular component. From now on, only series with annual seasonal cycles (or no cycles at all) are considered. In Subsection 2.1, a basic model for such time series is described. Methods for deciding whether this model is appropriate are discussed in Subsection 2.2. When the model is not appropriate, a transformation of the time series can sometimes be found that produces a time series for which the model may validly be used. Transformations of time series are discussed in Subsection 2.3.

2.1 Models for time series

The trend, seasonal and irregular components described in Section 1 were introduced to describe the main features of a time series. In fact, thinking of a time series in terms of its constituent parts is a fruitful approach, which can be used to develop models for time series. The idea is illustrated in Example 2.1.

Example 2.1 Building up a time series

A time series can be thought of as being built up from its trend, seasonal and irregular components. For example, consider the data in Table 2.1.

Table 2.1   Components of a time series

Time t and season		Trend component	Seasonal component	Irregular component	Total
1	Spring	100	+20	+6.4	126.4
2	Summer	110	−35	−9.2	65.8
3	Autumn	120	−15	+4.2	109.2
4	Winter	130	+30	+12.6	172.6
5	Spring	140	+20	−5.0	155.0
6	Summer	150	−35	+5.6	120.6
7	Autumn	160	−15	−6.0	139.0
8	Winter	170	+30	+2.2	202.2

These data are artificial, but might plausibly represent sales of a particular product for which demand varies seasonally, being higher in the winter and spring than in the summer and autumn.

The time t is listed in the first column, together with the season to which it corresponds. These data are quarterly. The trend component is in the second column. This describes how the level changes over time. In this example, the level increases linearly by 10 units each quarter.

The third column contains the seasonal component. The values repeat every four quarters: spring sales are boosted by 20 units, summer and autumn sales are depleted by 35 and 15 respectively, and winter sales are boosted by 30. Thus the values of the seasonal components for the four quarters, starting with spring, are +20, −35, −15 and +30. These values are called the **seasonal factors**. The seasonal factors of a time series sum to zero over one year: in this example, $20 − 35 − 15 + 30 = 0$. Note that the seasonal factors represent seasonal *departures* from the underlying level of sales.

The fourth column contains the irregular component. This is assumed to vary randomly around zero, according to some distribution. Adding together the three components (trend, seasonal and irregular) gives the overall value x_t, which is shown in the final column of Table 2.1.

This time series, with its various components, is shown in Figure 2.1.

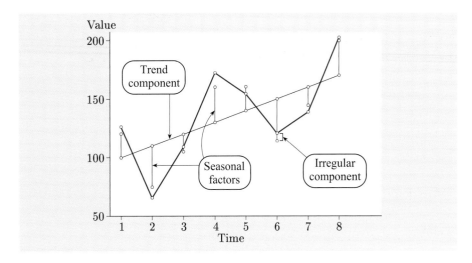

Figure 2.1   A time series built up from its components

The trend component is represented by the upward-sloping line in the centre of the diagram. The seasonal factors are represented as vertical lines, indicating the departures from the trend. The irregular component is manifested by the vertical distances between the points in the time series and the tips of the vertical lines. ◆

The idea illustrated in Example 2.1 of building up a time series from its constituent parts can be described in general terms as follows.

The trend component of a time series is denoted m_t: this describes how the level of the time series varies with t.

The seasonal component is denoted s_t and its period T. The values of the seasonal component repeat every T time points. Thus, if the time points t represent months, then $T = 12$ and

$$s_t = s_{t+12} \quad \text{for all } t.$$

If the time points t represent quarters, then $T = 4$ and

$$s_t = s_{t+4} \quad \text{for all } t.$$

In general, for a seasonal component with period T,

$$s_t = s_{t+T} \quad \text{for all } t.$$

Thus s_t takes only T different values, $s_1, s_2, \ldots, s_T$. These values are called the **seasonal factors**. These T seasonal factors represent departures from the trend, and sum to zero over a period:

$$s_1 + s_2 + \cdots + s_T = 0.$$

The sum of the trend component and the seasonal component gives the systematic (non-random) part of the time series, which is denoted μ_t. Thus

$$\mu_t = m_t + s_t.$$

The level and the trend component are closely related: the level at time t is the value of the trend component at time t.

All the seasonal cycles analysed in this book are annual, so the seasonal factors sum to zero over a year.

At each time point t, x_t may be regarded as an observation on some random variable X_t with mean $E(X_t) = \mu_t$. A simple model for X_t is

$$X_t = \mu_t + W_t,$$

where $W_t = X_t - \mu_t$ is a random variable with mean zero and variance σ^2. Note that in this model it is assumed that X_t has constant variance σ^2: $V(X_t) = \sigma^2$ for all t. The random variable W_t corresponds to the irregular component of the time series. Thus the overall model is

Upper-case letters X, Y, Z, W are used to represent random variables, and lower-case letters x, y, z, w are used to represent particular values of these random variables.

$$X_t = m_t + s_t + W_t.$$

The main difference between this model and models in other areas of statistics is that, for different time points t, the random variables W_t cannot generally be assumed to be independent.

This model is called the **additive decomposition model**. It is a *decomposition* model because it is based on a decomposition of the time series into distinct components, and *additive* because the various components are added together. Note that this model can also be used to represent time series with constant level — that is, models for which m_t is constant, $m_t = m$ for all t — and time series with no seasonal component, for which $s_t = 0$ for all t. The model is summarized in the following box.

The additive decomposition model

The **additive decomposition model** for a time series X_t is

$$X_t = m_t + s_t + W_t, \quad t = 1, 2, \ldots,$$

where m_t is the **trend component**, s_t is the **seasonal component** of period T, and W_t is the **irregular** (or random) **component**.

The seasonal component satisfies

$$s_t = s_{t+T} \quad \text{for all } t,$$
$$s_1 + \cdots + s_T = 0.$$

The distinct values $s_1, \ldots, s_T$ are the **seasonal factors.**

The irregular component W_t has mean 0 and variance σ^2:

$$E(W_t) = 0, \quad V(W_t) = \sigma^2.$$

Activity 2.1   Seasonal factors

One of the following sequences of numbers represents the first few values of the seasonal component for a quarterly additive decomposition time series model. The others do not. For each sequence, state whether or not it represents the seasonal component, giving a reason for your answer.

(a) $-2, +4, +3, -5, -3, +5, +4, -6, \ldots$.

(b) $+3, -1, -2, 0, +3, -1, -2, 0, \ldots$.

(c) $-4, +3, +3, -1, -4, +3, +3, -1, \ldots$.

2.2 Additive models and multiplicative models

If the random variable X_t is necessarily positive, as is often the case, then an alternative way of combining the trend component m_t, the seasonal component s_t and the irregular component W_t is to multiply them together:

$$X_t = m_t \times s_t \times W_t.$$

This model is called the **multiplicative decomposition model**. The systematic component is $\mu_t = m_t s_t$ and the irregular component W_t is X_t/μ_t. The seasonal component of a multiplicative model is defined differently from that of the additive model. For the multiplicative model,

$$s_t = s_{t+T} \quad \text{for all } t,$$
$$s_1 \times s_2 \times \cdots \times s_T = 1.$$

Time series generated by additive models and multiplicative models often look quite different. This is illustrated in Figure 2.2.

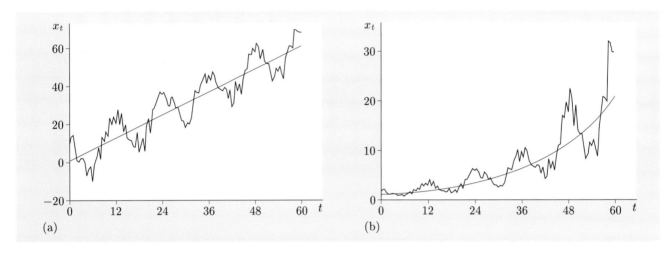

(a) (b)

Figure 2.2   Time series generated by decomposition models: (a) additive (b) multiplicative

For the time series in Figure 2.2(a), which was generated using an additive model, the seasonal fluctuations do not vary in size systematically with the value of m_t, the level of the time series at time t. Thus the seasonal fluctuations are of roughly the same size whether the level m_t is large or small. Similarly, the irregular fluctuations are roughly of the same size, whatever the value of the systematic component $m_t + s_t$.

The word 'fluctuations' is used here in a non-technical sense. 'Seasonal fluctuations' and 'irregular fluctuations' are not technical terms.

In contrast, for the time series in Figure 2.2(b), the size of the seasonal fluctuations is proportional to m_t, the level at time t: the larger the value of m_t, the larger are the seasonal fluctuations. Note that the change in the size of the seasonal fluctuations is not due to a change in the seasonal component s_t. It arises because m_t and s_t are multiplied together. Similarly, the size of the irregular fluctuations is proportional to $m_t \times s_t$: the larger this is, the larger are the irregular fluctuations.

These differences between the appearance of time series with an additive structure and time series with a multiplicative structure may be used to identify when an additive model is appropriate. If an additive model is not appropriate, then a multiplicative model may be, although it is possible that neither is appropriate.

Example 2.2   Is an additive model appropriate?

Clostridium difficile is a bacterium that causes diarrhoea. It is of particular concern in hospitals. Figure 2.3(a) shows the time plot for the weekly number of reported cases of infection by *Clostridium difficile* in England and Wales between the middle of 1996 and the middle of 2003.

These data and other data in this book on infections in the UK were provided by the Health Protection Agency Centre for Infections, London.

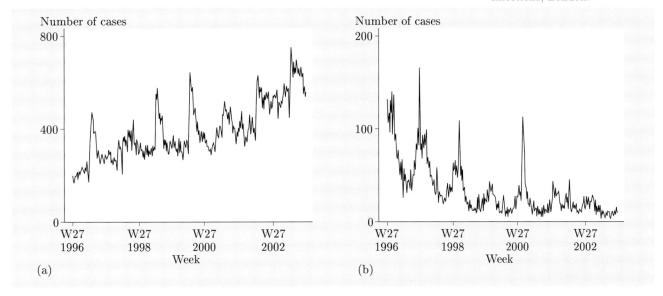

Figure 2.3   Weekly reports of infections, 1996–2003: (a) *Clostridium difficile* (b) *Salmonella Typhimurium* DT104

There is an increasing trend (which is most likely due at least in part to improvements in the reporting of infections). There is also some evidence of seasonality, as shown by the peaks separated by a period of about 52 weeks. The magnitude of the seasonal fluctuations, and the size of the irregular fluctuations, do not appear to vary according to the level of the series: they are not markedly greater at the later end of the data series (when the average weekly number of reports is about 500) than at the beginning (when there are about 250 reports per week). This suggests that an additive model may be appropriate for this time series.

Salmonella Typhimurium DT104 is a bacterium that causes food poisoning. Figure 2.3(b) shows the time plot for the weekly number of reports of *Salmonella Typhimurium* DT104 between the middle of 1996 and the middle of 2003. In this case there is a broadly downward trend, from about 100 reports per week on average to about 10 per week. There is also marked seasonality, as shown by the peaks at intervals of about 52 weeks. However, in this series, the seasonal fluctuations appear to be greater in size in the earlier part of the series, when the weekly numbers of reports are larger, than in the later part of the series. The irregular week-to-week variation may also be greater during the earlier part of the series, though it is more difficult to be sure of this from the plot. Nevertheless, it is unlikely that an additive model will be appropriate for this series. On the other hand, a multiplicative model may be appropriate, though this is not guaranteed.   ♦

As in many other areas of statistics, deciding whether or not a particular model is appropriate is as much an art as a science! Activity 2.2 will give you some practice in deciding whether or not an additive decomposition model is appropriate.

Activity 2.2   Travel and temperatures: choosing a model

The time plots of two time series that were introduced in Section 1 are reproduced in Figure 2.4.

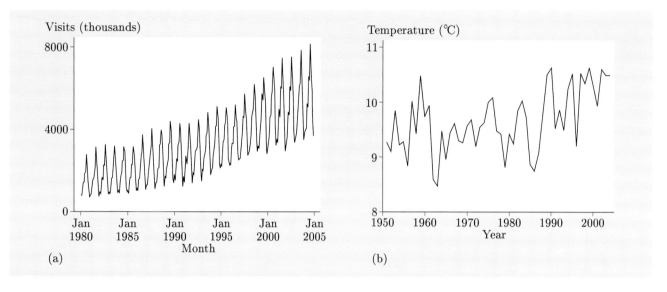

Figure 2.4   (a) Visits overseas by UK residents (b) Annual average temperatures (°C)

Figure 2.4(a) shows the (highly seasonal) time series of monthly visits overseas by UK residents. Figure 2.4(b) shows the time series of annual temperatures in Central England, 1951–2004; this time series is non-seasonal.

These time plots were shown previously as Figures 1.1 and 1.9.

For each of these time series, discuss whether or not an additive model is likely to be appropriate.

2.3   Transforming time series

Consider the multiplicative model $X_t = m_t \times s_t \times W_t$. Let Y_t denote the time series of logarithms: $Y_t = \log X_t$. Then

Natural logarithms (that is, to base e) are used throughout this book.

$$Y_t = \log X_t$$
$$= \log (m_t \times s_t \times W_t)$$
$$= \log m_t + \log s_t + \log W_t.$$

Thus the model for Y_t is additive, with trend component $\log m_t$, seasonal component $\log s_t$ and irregular component $\log W_t$. It follows that if a multiplicative model is appropriate for the time series X_t, then an additive model is appropriate for the time series of logarithms, $Y_t = \log X_t$. Thus, by taking logarithms, a time series for which a multiplicative model is appropriate can be transformed into a time series for which an additive model is appropriate.

Example 2.3   Rotavirus infections

Rotavirus infection causes diarrhoea and, in poor countries, is a major cause of infant and child mortality. The time series of weekly reports of rotavirus infection in England and Wales from the middle of 1996 to the middle of 1998 is shown in Figure 2.5.

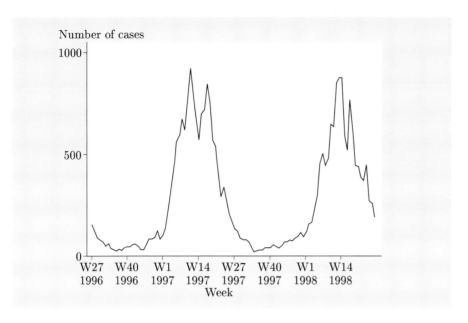

Figure 2.5   Time series of weekly reports of rotavirus infection

This time series does not display any clear upward or downward trend, but there is substantial seasonality. Week 14 of each year corresponds to early April, and hence the seasonal peak occurs in late winter and early spring. Since there is no trend, a decision as to whether or not an additive model might be appropriate must be based solely on the irregular component.

The seasonal effect dominates in Figure 2.5. Nevertheless, it is apparent that the irregular fluctuations are less marked in the troughs than during the seasonal peaks: the big gashes at the tops of the peaks are much deeper than the little wiggles at the bottoms of the troughs. Thus an additive model is likely to be inappropriate for this time series.

Is a multiplicative model appropriate? This can be investigated by transforming the time series using logarithms: each value x_t is replaced by its logarithm. The time series of logarithms of weekly reports of rotavirus infection is shown in Figure 2.6.

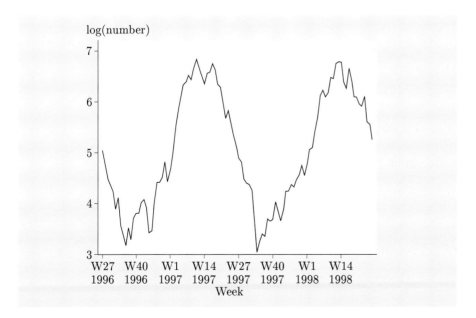

Figure 2.6   Logarithms of weekly reports of rotavirus infection

The transformed time series displays the same seasonal periodicity as the original time series shown in Figure 2.5. However, the irregular fluctuations are now

23

roughly of the same magnitude wherever they occur in the series: in particular, they are roughly of the same size in the troughs and at the peaks of the seasonal cycle.

This suggests that an additive model is appropriate for the log transformed series. It follows that a multiplicative model is appropriate for the original, untransformed, rotavirus time series.   ◆

Activity 2.3   Visits overseas: logarithms

In Activity 2.2, you found that an additive model is not appropriate for the time series of monthly numbers of visits overseas by UK residents, because the size of the seasonal fluctuations increases with the level of the series. The time series of logarithms of numbers of visits overseas is shown in Figure 2.7.

The logarithms are taken of the numbers in *thousands*.

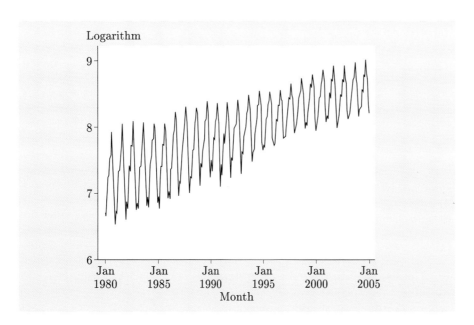

Figure 2.7   Logarithms of numbers of visits overseas by UK residents

(a) Is an additive model appropriate for the time series shown in Figure 2.7? Explain your reasoning.

(b) What do you conclude about the validity of using either an additive model or a multiplicative model to represent the time series of monthly visits overseas?

Activity 2.3 shows that some time series cannot be described adequately either by an additive model or by a multiplicative model. One way of overcoming this difficulty is to extend the class of models available. For example, consider the model

$$X_t = m_t \times s_t + W_t.$$

This model has a multiplicative seasonal component and an additive irregular component, so it is neither purely additive nor purely multiplicative. There are many other possibilities.

A simpler approach is to try to find a transformation other than the log transformation which, when applied to the time series, produces a series for which an additive model can validly be used. This is the approach that will be used in this book. Transformations that are commonly used include the **power transformations**:

$$Y_t = X_t^a, \quad a = \ldots, \tfrac{1}{4}, \tfrac{1}{3}, \tfrac{1}{2}, 2, 3, \ldots .$$

It is important to emphasize that it is not *always* possible to find a transformation such that the transformed series may be represented adequately by an additive model.

Example 2.4   Visits overseas: square roots

Figure 2.8 shows the time series of square roots of the numbers of visits overseas by UK residents: $y_t = x_t^{1/2}$.

The square roots are taken of the numbers in *thousands*.

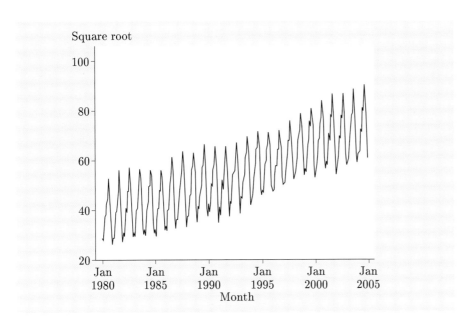

Figure 2.8   Square roots of numbers of visits overseas by UK residents

The seasonal fluctuations are of roughly the same size whatever the level of the series. However, it is not possible to tell from Figure 2.8 whether this is also true of the irregular fluctuations. Thus it is not possible to conclude that an additive model is appropriate for this transformed series, only that it *may* be appropriate.   ♦

Activity 2.4   Transforming the salmonella time series

In Figure 2.3(b), the time series of weekly reports of *Salmonella Typhimurium* DT104 was presented. The time series was discussed in Example 2.2, where it was concluded that an additive model is unlikely to be appropriate as the seasonal fluctuations vary with the level of the series. However, it was not clear whether the irregular fluctuations also vary with the level. Two transformations of this time series are shown in Figure 2.9.

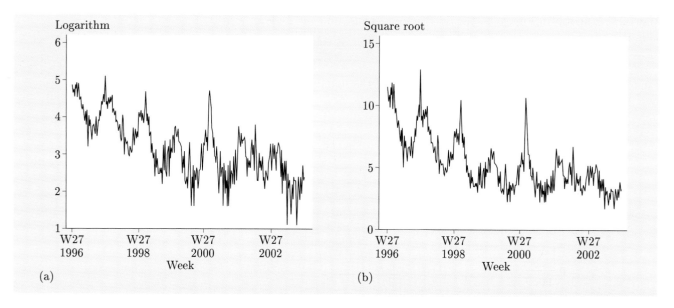

Figure 2.9   Transformations of weekly reports of *Salmonella Typhimurium* DT104: (a) logarithm (b) square root

(a)   Describe the effect of the log transformation on the seasonal and irregular variation.

(b)   Describe the effect of the square root transformation on the seasonal and irregular variation.

(c)   In your opinion, which of the two time series in Figure 2.9 would it be more appropriate to describe by an additive model?

Summary of Section 2

In this section, the additive decomposition model and the multiplicative decomposition model have been introduced. You have learned how to use a time plot to decide whether or not an additive model is appropriate for a time series. You have seen that the log transformation transforms a multiplicative model into an additive model. The use of transformations other than the log transformation to produce a series for which an additive model may be appropriate has been discussed briefly.

Exercises on Section 2

Exercise 2.1   Beer consumption

The time series of quarterly beer consumption in the UK, 1991–2004, was introduced in Activity 1.3. The time plot of this series is shown in Figure 1.3.

Discuss whether an additive model is appropriate for these data.

Exercise 2.2   Company sales

The time plot of monthly sales by a company between January 1965 and May 1971 is shown in Figure 2.10. (The company name and the units in which sales are measured have been concealed.)

O'Donovan, T.M. (1983) *Short Term Forecasting: An Introduction to the Box–Jenkins Approach*. Wiley, Chichester.

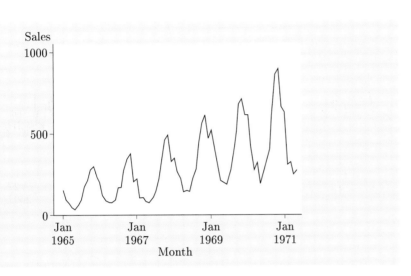

Figure 2.10   Monthly sales figures, 1965–1971

(a) Is an additive model suitable for this time series? Explain your reasoning.

Two transformations of the time series are shown in Figure 2.11.

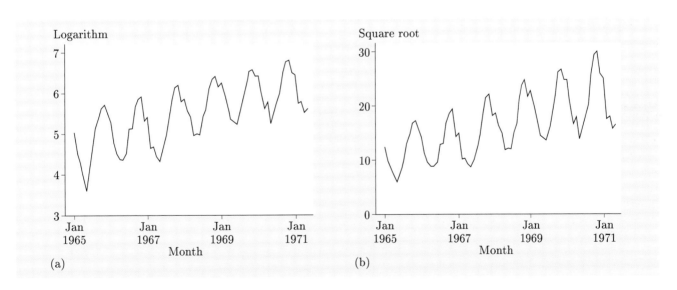

Figure 2.11   Transformed sales figures: (a) logarithm (b) square root

(b) Figure 2.11(a) shows the time plot of the logarithms of the monthly sales. The time plot of the square roots of the monthly sales is shown in Figure 2.11(b). In your opinion, which of the two time series in Figure 2.11 would it be more appropriate to describe by an additive model?

3 Displaying time series data in SPSS

In this section, you will learn how to enter, display and transform time series data in SPSS.

Refer to Chapter 1 of Computer Book 2 for the work in this section.

Summary of Section 3

In this section, you have learned how to enter time series data in SPSS and how to define dates. You have also learned how to obtain time plots, and how to transform time series. You have used these methods to investigate whether an additive or a multiplicative model might be appropriate for a time series.

4 Estimating the components of a time series

In this section, a method for estimating the components of a time series that can be described by an additive model is discussed. In Subsection 4.1, a technique for estimating the trend component of a non-seasonal time series is introduced. In Subsection 4.2, this technique is modified and applied to seasonal time series; this leads to a method for estimating the seasonal component of a seasonal time series. In Subsection 4.3, the techniques described in Subsections 4.1 and 4.2 are combined to give a method for decomposing a time series into seasonal, trend and irregular components.

4.1 Estimating the trend component

In this subsection, time series that can be described by an additive model with only a trend component and an irregular component are considered. This model, which does not have a seasonal component, is the **non-seasonal additive model**:

$$X_t = m_t + W_t.$$

Sometimes the trend in a time series is clear from looking at a time plot. However, when this is not the case, in order to describe the trend, the trend component m_t must be estimated.

The trend may be obscured by the fluctuations of the irregular component W_t, especially if the variation in m_t is small compared to σ, the standard deviation of W_t. In this context, the irregular component is sometimes referred to as **noise**. The larger the standard deviation of W_t, the more the irregular component obscures the trend, and the noisier the series is said to be.

One way to reduce the noise is to replace each value x_t with the average of x_t and its neighbouring values. This is illustrated in Example 4.1.

Example 4.1 Reducing noise

The time series of annual average temperatures in Central England, 1659–2004, was shown in Figure 1.2. The time plot is reproduced in Figure 4.1(a).

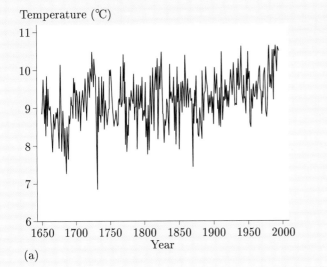

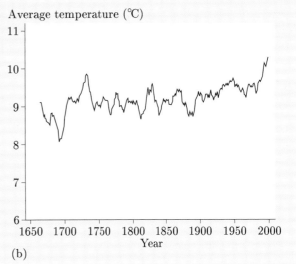

(a) (b)

Figure 4.1   Annual average temperatures (°C), Central England

This is a very noisy series: the irregular year-to-year fluctuations are large and tend to obscure the underlying trend. To reduce the noise, the series was transformed as follows. For each year t, the value x_t was replaced by the average of eleven values, corresponding to the temperatures in year t, in the five years preceding year t, and in the five years following year t. Thus, for example, the value for 1999 was replaced by the average of the values for years 1994 to 2004. This transformed series is shown in Figure 4.1(b).

The time plot in Figure 4.1(b) is much less jagged than the time plot of the original series in Figure 4.1(a). So it is easier to identify underlying patterns from Figure 4.1(b) than from Figure 4.1(a). These patterns can now be summarized as follows. Temperatures were unusually low prior to about 1700, they fluctuated around an average value that remained roughly constant from 1700 to 1900, and they tended to increase after about 1900.   ◆

The transformation described in Example 4.1 is called a **simple moving average** (or just a moving average). It can be written as

$$Y_t = \tfrac{1}{11}(X_{t-5} + \cdots + X_t + \cdots + X_{t+5}). \tag{4.1}$$

This transformation has the effect of reducing the standard deviation of the irregular component, hence producing a less jagged plot. This process of noise reduction is called **smoothing**.

Since eleven values are used in the expression in (4.1), this transformation is said to be a moving average of **order** (or **span**) 11. For the purpose of smoothing time series, only moving averages for which the order is an odd number will be used. These are said to be **centred** on the middle value.

The definition of a simple moving average of arbitrary odd order is given in the following box.

Simple moving average

The **simple moving average** of order $2q + 1$ centred on t is given by the transformation

$$MA(t) = \frac{1}{2q+1}\left(X_{t-q} + \cdots + X_t + \cdots + X_{t+q}\right). \qquad (4.2)$$

Example 4.2   A moving average of order 5

The first five values of the Central England temperatures time series are reproduced in Table 4.1.

For a simple moving average of order 5, $q = 2$, so the moving average value for the year 1661 is

$$
\begin{aligned}
y_{1661} &= \tfrac{1}{5}\left(x_{1661-2} + x_{1661-1} + x_{1661} + x_{1661+1} + x_{1661+2}\right)\\
&= \tfrac{1}{5}(8.83 + 9.08 + 9.75 + 9.50 + 8.58)\\
&= 9.148. \quad \blacklozenge
\end{aligned}
$$

Table 4.1   Five values of the Central England temperatures time series

Year	Average temperature
1659	8.83
1660	9.08
1661	9.75
1662	9.50
1663	8.58

Activity 4.1   Calculating a simple moving average

(a) Use a simple moving average of order 3, and the data in Table 4.1, to calculate moving average values for the years 1660, 1661 and 1662.

(b) Explain why the values of a simple moving average of order 3 cannot be calculated for the years 1659 and 1663 from the data in Table 4.1.

(c) For which years can a moving average of order 5 be calculated from the data in Table 4.1?

In Activity 4.1, you found that, for a moving average of order 3, the values corresponding to the first time point and the last time point cannot be calculated. In general, for a moving average of order $2q + 1$, the values for the first q and the last q time points cannot be calculated. In practice, this is not a problem as the order of the moving average is usually much shorter than the time series.

The smoothing effect of moving averages of different orders is illustrated in Example 4.3.

Example 4.3 Temperature of a chemical process

Figure 4.2 shows the time series of temperatures, in degrees Fahrenheit, of a chemical process at intervals of two minutes.

Montgomery, D.C., Johnson, L.A. and Gardiner, J.S. (1990) *Forecasting and Time Series Analysis.* Second Edition. McGraw-Hill, New York.

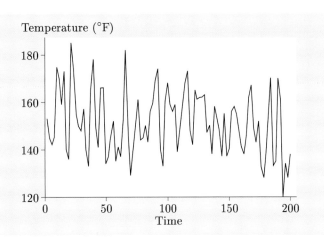

Figure 4.2 Temperature (°F) of a chemical process over time (minutes)

Moving averages of orders 3 and 21 are used to smooth this time series. The results are shown in Figure 4.3.

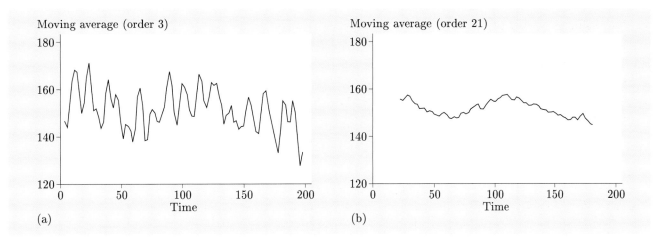

Figure 4.3 Moving averages: (a) order 3 (b) order 21

Note that the vertical scale used in Figures 4.3(a) and 4.3(b) is the same as the one used for the unsmoothed series in Figure 4.2. Using the same scale for the moving averages as for the original time series is essential in order to assess the degree of smoothing.

Compare Figure 4.3(a) with Figure 4.2. Notice that the moving average of order 3 has reduced the size of the fluctuations. However, substantial noise remains in the time series, and the underlying trend is still not very clear. The moving average of order 21 in Figure 4.3(b) has smoothed the series much more drastically. The remaining fluctuations are much smaller, and the overall trend is now much clearer. The trend can be summarized as follows: the mean temperatures dropped over the first hour, then rose for about three-quarters of an hour, before dropping again. ♦

31

The higher the order of the moving average that is used, the greater is the smoothing effect produced. With a suitable degree of smoothing — that is, with a suitable choice of the order of the moving average — the moving average provides an estimate of the trend component m_t; this is denoted $\widehat{m}_t$. Thus

$$\widehat{m}_t = \frac{1}{2q+1}\left(x_{t-q} + \cdots + x_t + \cdots + x_{t+q}\right).$$

Choosing the right amount of smoothing — that is, choosing an appropriate value for the order $2q+1$ of the moving average — is not a simple task, and is to a large extent a matter of judgement. If the order of a moving average is too low, then not enough of the noise will be removed to reveal the underlying trend clearly; this is described as **under-smoothing** the data. On the other hand, if the order of a moving average is too high, there is a risk that variations of interest in the trend itself will be ironed out. This is described as **over-smoothing** the data.

To see how under-smoothing and over-smoothing arise, consider again the non-seasonal additive model

$$X_t = m_t + W_t.$$

When the observed values of X_t are averaged, both the trend component m_t and the irregular component W_t are averaged. Averaging the values of W_t reduces the standard deviation of the irregular term, and hence reduces the noise; this result of smoothing is desirable. However, by averaging the trend component, some important detail of the trend may be lost, and this would be undesirable. Under-smoothing arises when the noise is not sufficiently reduced to reveal the trend; over-smoothing arises when important detail in the trend is smoothed out.

The aim is to smooth by just the right amount, so as to eliminate most of the noise while leaving the trend largely unaffected. Unfortunately, a general rule for achieving this is not readily available. It is usually a good idea to try moving averages of several different orders before attempting to summarize an underlying trend. Activity 4.2 will give you some practice at choosing how much to smooth a time series.

Activity 4.2   Choosing the order of a moving average

Figure 4.4 shows 197 successive readings of the concentration level of a chemical process, taken at two-hourly intervals.

Box, G.E.P. and Jenkins, G.M. (1976) *Time Series Analysis: Forecasting and Control.* Holden-Day, San Francisco.

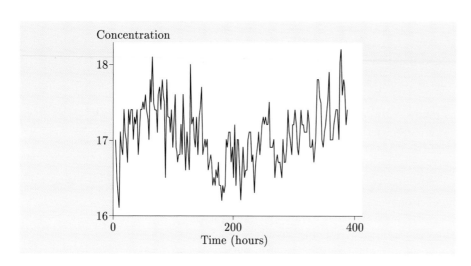

Figure 4.4   The concentration level of a chemical process

The time series is non-seasonal, but very noisy.

Moving averages of orders 51, 25, 11 and 3 were used to smooth the series. The results are shown in Figure 4.5.

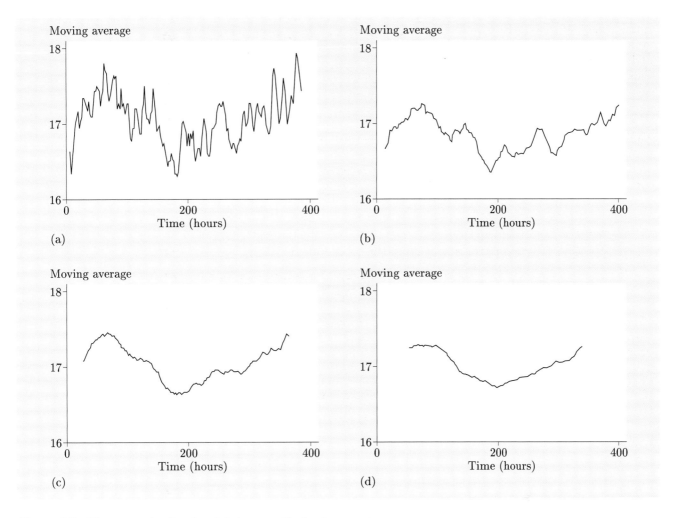

Figure 4.5 The concentration level data smoothed using moving averages

(a) Which moving average was used to produce the smoothed series in each of the four time plots shown in Figure 4.5?

(b) In your view, which of the moving averages result in under-smoothing of the time series? Which produce over-smoothing? Which smooth the series by about the right amount?

4.2 Estimating the seasonal component

In Subsection 4.1, simple (centred) moving averages were used to estimate the trend component of a non-seasonal time series. In this subsection, moving averages will be used to estimate the seasonal component of a seasonal time series.

Consider a seasonal time series X_t that can be described using the additive model

$$X_t = m_t + s_t + W_t.$$

The first step is to find an initial estimate of the trend component m_t that is not unduly influenced by the seasonal component s_t. A reasonable starting point would be to use a simple moving average with order equal to the period T of the seasonal cycle. Such a moving average would smooth out the seasonal variation, as the annual highs and lows would cancel out.

The notation X_t is used both for a time series and for the random variable representing the element of the series at time t.

For example, suppose that the data are quarterly, so that $T = 4$, and a smoothed value is required for summer 2006. The period is an even number, but to centre the moving average on summer 2006, an odd order is required. A simple moving average of order 5 (say) would average over winter, spring, summer and autumn 2006 and winter 2007: thus winter would be counted twice. This problem can be overcome by using a different type of moving average, called a **weighted moving average**. In this example, if the two winter values are given half the weight of the other values, then each season is equally weighted. In general, for a quarterly time series X_t, the following transformation is used:

$$SA(t) = \tfrac{1}{4}(0.5X_{t-2} + X_{t-1} + X_t + X_{t+1} + 0.5X_{t+2}).$$ (4.3)

The S in the notation $SA(t)$ is for Seasonal.

Similarly, if the series X_t is monthly, so that $T = 12$, the following transformation is used:

$$SA(t) = \tfrac{1}{12}(0.5X_{t-6} + X_{t-5} + \cdots + X_t + \cdots + X_{t+5} + 0.5X_{t+6}).$$ (4.4)

This ensures that each month is equally weighted.

Since the seasonal factors add up to zero over a seasonal cycle, when applied to an additive time series with seasonal component s_t, the transformations $SA(t)$ in (4.3) and (4.4) give the same result as they would if there were no seasonal component. Thus these transformations remove the seasonal effect. This is illustrated in Example 4.4.

Example 4.4   Visits overseas: smoothing out the seasonal component

In Example 2.4, you saw that an additive model may be appropriate for the monthly time series of square roots of numbers of visits overseas by UK residents. The time plot for this time series is reproduced in Figure 4.6(a).

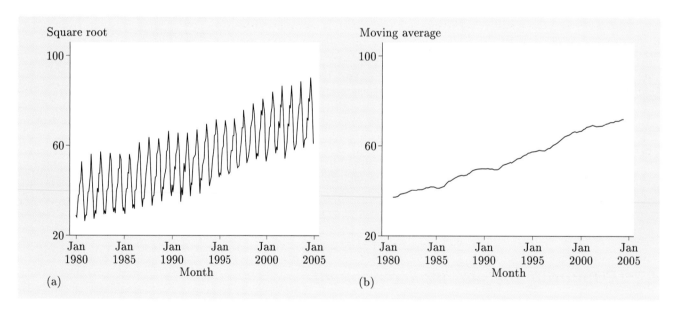

Figure 4.6   Square roots of numbers of visits overseas: (a) original data (b) after applying the moving average

The time series displays very marked seasonality. Figure 4.6(b) shows the time series obtained by applying the transformation (4.4) to this time series. The seasonal variation has been smoothed out of the series, leaving the (smoothed) underlying trend and some irregular variation from month to month.

Since the values s_t repeat every twelve time points, and $s_1 + s_2 + \cdots + s_{12} = 0$, for each t,

$$0.5s_{t-6} + s_{t-5} + \cdots + s_t + \cdots + s_{t+5} + 0.5s_{t+6} = 0.$$

Hence the transformation is effective in removing the seasonal component. ◆

The transformations (4.3) and (4.4) are examples of *weighted moving averages*. The general weighted moving average of odd order is defined in the following box.

Weighted moving average

A **weighted moving average** of order $2q + 1$ has the form

$$MA(t) = a_{-q}X_{t-q} + \cdots + a_{-1}X_{t-1} + a_0X_t + a_1X_{t+1} + \cdots + a_qX_{t+q},$$

where the **weights** a_j, $j = -q, -q+1, \ldots, q$, add up to 1.

The weighted moving averages in (4.3) and (4.4) are denoted $SA(t)$ rather than $MA(t)$ because of their particular use in smoothing out seasonal variation: the S is for Seasonal.

The simple moving average (4.2), which was introduced in Subsection 4.1, is a weighted moving average in which the weights a_j are all equal to $(2q + 1)^{-1}$. Just as simple moving averages can be used to smooth time series, so can weighted moving averages.

Activity 4.3 Weighted moving averages

(a) Give two reasons why the following transformation is not a weighted moving average:

$$z_t = 0.1x_{t-2} + 0.3x_{t-1} + 0.1x_t^2 + 0.3x_{t+1} + 0.1x_{t+2}.$$

(b) Suppose that bimonthly time series data are available, with seasonal period $T = 6$. Write down an appropriate weighted moving average of order 7 for smoothing out the seasonal variation.

In Example 4.4, you saw that the weighted moving average $SA(t)$ with appropriate order smooths out the seasonality from a seasonal time series $X_t = m_t + s_t + W_t$: the result is the same as if the transformation had been applied to the series $m_t + W_t$. In Subsection 4.1, you saw that a simple centred moving average provides an estimate of the trend component of a non-seasonal time series. Thus the weighted moving average $SA(t)$ provides an estimate of the trend component m_t of the seasonal time series X_t:

$$\widehat{m}_t = SA(t).$$

Now consider the differences between the original series $X_t = m_t + s_t + W_t$ and $SA(t) = \widehat{m}_t$. These differences will be denoted Y_t. Since $Y_t = X_t - SA(t)$, we have

$$Y_t = m_t + s_t + W_t - \widehat{m}_t$$
$$= s_t + W_t + (m_t - \widehat{m}_t)$$
$$= s_t + W_t', \quad \text{say.}$$

The term $W_t' = W_t + (m_t - \widehat{m}_t)$ is a new irregular component. Thus the time series Y_t has no trend component: it consists of the seasonal component of the original series X_t and some irregular variation.

Example 4.5   Visits overseas: removing the trend component

In Example 4.4, the seasonal component was smoothed out of the monthly time series x_t of (square roots of) numbers of visits overseas by UK citizens by applying the weighted moving average $SA(t)$. The series of differences $y_t = x_t - SA(t)$ is shown in Figure 4.7.

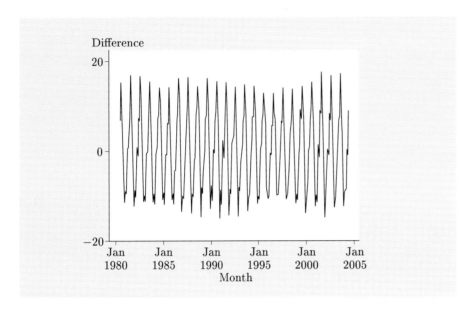

Figure 4.7   Visits overseas data: the differences $y_t = x_t - SA(t)$

The trend has been removed, leaving the series

$$y_t = s_t + w_t'.$$

The irregular component is apparent from the slight variation in the width of the seasonal fluctuations. In order to estimate the seasonal component of the original time series, this remaining irregular variation must be removed.   ◆

In general, the irregular variation W_t' may be removed as follows. For each season, all the values of Y_t corresponding to that season are gathered together, and their average is calculated. The averages are called the **raw seasonal factors** and are denoted F_j, $j = 1, 2, \ldots, T$.

For example, for a monthly series, F_{January}, the raw seasonal factor for January, is given by

$$F_{\text{January}} = \frac{\text{sum of the values } y_t \text{ for January}}{\text{number of January values}}.$$

The corresponding values for February, March, and so on, are obtained in a similar way. Similarly, for a quarterly series, for each quarter, all the values of Y_t for that quarter are averaged to give the raw seasonal factor for the quarter.

The seasonal factors $s_1, \ldots, s_T$ sum to zero over one seasonal cycle, so to estimate the seasonal factors, the average of the F_j is subtracted from each raw seasonal factor. For example, for a monthly series, the seasonal factor for January is estimated by

$$\widehat{s}_{\text{January}} = F_{\text{January}} - \overline{F},$$

where $\overline{F} = (F_{\text{January}} + \cdots + F_{\text{December}})/12$. The seasonal factors for the other seasons are estimated in a similar way. This method is illustrated in Example 4.6.

Example 4.6 Visits overseas: estimating the seasonal component

For the monthly time series of (square roots of) numbers of visits overseas, there were 24 values of Y_t for each month. The values of F_j for these data are given in Table 4.2.

Table 4.2 Estimating the seasonal factors

Month j	F_j	$\widehat{s}_j$
January	−9.5809	−9.576
February	−10.2581	−10.254
March	−5.4079	−5.403
April	−0.6274	−0.623
May	0.4188	0.423
June	6.5996	6.604
July	7.7319	7.736
August	15.2347	15.239
September	10.5442	10.549
October	4.8317	4.836
November	−7.0544	−7.050
December	−12.4856	−12.481

The average of the twelve values F_j corresponding to the months January to December is −0.004 45, so $\overline{F} = -0.004\,45$, and hence the estimated seasonal factors are given by $\widehat{s}_j = F_j + 0.004\,45$. The estimated seasonal factors $\widehat{s}_j$ rounded to three decimal places are also shown in Table 4.2. The estimated seasonal component of the time series comprises the estimated seasonal factors repeated over successive periods. This is shown in Figure 4.8.

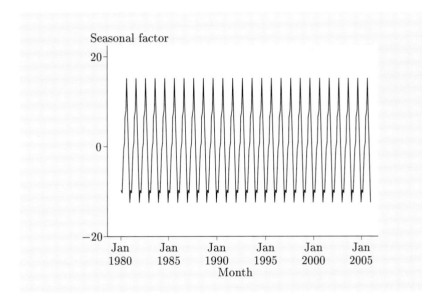

Figure 4.8 The estimated seasonal component for the visits overseas time series

Note how the series in Figure 4.8 differs from that in Figure 4.7: the irregular variation has been removed, and the estimated seasonal component now repeats exactly every twelve months, as required.

The values $\widehat{s}_j$ in Table 4.2 represent the estimated average seasonal departures from the underlying trend. The largest value is positive and corresponds to the month of August; the smallest value is negative and corresponds to December. These estimated seasonal factors show that the series peaks in August and is lowest in December. ◆

In this book, you will not be required to estimate the components of a seasonal time series by hand: although the calculations are not difficult, they are tedious, so they are best done by a computer. However, you will be required to interpret plots corresponding to the various stages of a decomposition of a seasonal time series into components, and to interpret estimated trends, raw seasonal factors and estimated seasonal factors. The stages involved in estimating the seasonal factors are summarized in the following box.

Estimating the seasonal component of an additive model

For a seasonal time series X_t, which may be described by an additive model, and for which the seasonal period is T (an even number), the seasonal component s_t may be estimated as follows.

◇ First, the series is smoothed using a suitable weighted moving average. For example, if $T = 12$,

$$SA(t) = \tfrac{1}{12}(0.5x_{t-6} + x_{t-5} + \cdots + x_t + \cdots + x_5 + 0.5x_{t+6});$$

or, if $T = 4$,

$$SA(t) = \tfrac{1}{4}(0.5x_{t-2} + x_{t-1} + x_t + x_{t+1} + 0.5x_{t+2}).$$

◇ Next, the series of differences $y_t = x_t - SA(t)$ is obtained.

◇ The **raw seasonal factors** $F_j, j = 1, \ldots, T$, are calculated as follows: for season j, F_j is the average of the values of y_t corresponding to that season.

◇ The average $\overline{F}$ of the raw seasonal factors F_j is obtained.

◇ The **seasonal factors** $s_1, s_2, \ldots, s_T$ are estimated by

$$\widehat{s}_j = F_j - \overline{F}, \quad j = 1, 2, \ldots, T.$$

Activity 4.4 will give you some practice at describing and interpreting the results at various stages in the estimation of the seasonal component of a time series.

Activity 4.4   *Beer consumption*

In Activity 1.3, the time series of quarterly beer consumption in the UK between the first quarter of 1991 and the second quarter of 2004 was introduced. The time plot shown in Figure 1.3 is reproduced in Figure 4.9(a).

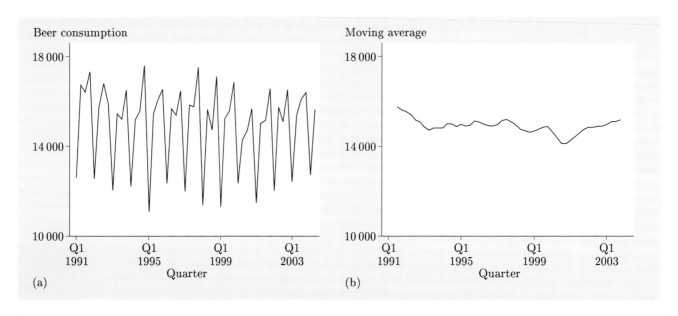

Figure 4.9   Quarterly beer consumption (in thousands of hectolitres), 1991–2004

This time series can be described adequately by an additive model, so the decomposition method described in this subsection can be applied. Figure 4.9(b) shows the series after smoothing with the weighted moving average $SA(t)$ of order 5. The raw seasonal factors F_j are given in Table 4.3.

(a) Briefly describe the trend shown in Figure 4.9(b).

(b) In two sentences, explain how the raw seasonal factors F_j are obtained from the series shown in Figure 4.9(a) and Figure 4.9(b).

(c) Use the raw seasonal factors F_j, which are given in Table 4.3, to obtain estimates $\widehat{s}_j$ of the seasonal factors.

(d) Interpret the estimated seasonal factors.

See Exercise 2.1.

Table 4.3 The raw seasonal factors F_j

Quarter j	F_j
1 January–March	−2949.41
2 April–June	500.18
3 July–September	647.19
4 October–December	1760.50

4.3 Seasonally adjusted series

In Subsection 4.1, you learned how to estimate the trend component for a non-seasonal time series; and in Subsection 4.2, you learned how to estimate the seasonal component for a seasonal time series. In this subsection, these methods are combined to estimate the seasonal, trend and irregular components of a seasonal time series.

Suppose that a time series may be described by the seasonal additive decomposition model

$$X_t = m_t + s_t + W_t.$$

The first stage in breaking down the time series into components is to estimate the seasonal factors (as described in Subsection 4.2). This produces an estimate $\widehat{s}_t$ of the seasonal component. This estimate is then used to obtain the **seasonally adjusted** series, which is denoted Z_t:

$$Z_t = X_t - \widehat{s}_t$$
$$= m_t + W_t + (s_t - \widehat{s}_t)$$
$$= m_t + W_t'.$$

The term $W_t' = W_t + (s_t - \widehat{s}_t)$ is a new irregular component.

The seasonally adjusted series Z_t has no seasonal component, only a trend component and an irregular component. Since the seasonal effect has been removed, the seasonally adjusted series can be used to make direct comparisons between levels in adjacent time periods. Many economic series (such as those for some indices of inflation and economic activity) are seasonally adjusted in order to reveal underlying trends.

The seasonal adjustment method used for economic time series is usually more complicated than that described here, but the principle is the same.

The seasonally adjusted time series can be analysed using the methods of Subsection 4.1: for example, an estimate $\widehat{m}_t$ of the trend component m_t can be obtained by smoothing the seasonally adjusted series Z_t. If required, the irregular component of the original series can be estimated by subtracting $\widehat{m}_t$, the estimate of m_t, from Z_t, the seasonally adjusted series:

$$\widehat{W}_t = Z_t - \widehat{m}_t.$$

This completes the decomposition of the original series into components:

$$X_t = \widehat{m}_t + \widehat{s}_t + \widehat{W}_t.$$

Example 4.7   Visits overseas: the seasonally adjusted series

The seasonal factors of the time series x_t of (square roots of) numbers of visits overseas by UK residents were estimated in Example 4.6. The seasonally adjusted series $z_t = x_t - \widehat{s}_t$ is shown in Figure 4.10(a).

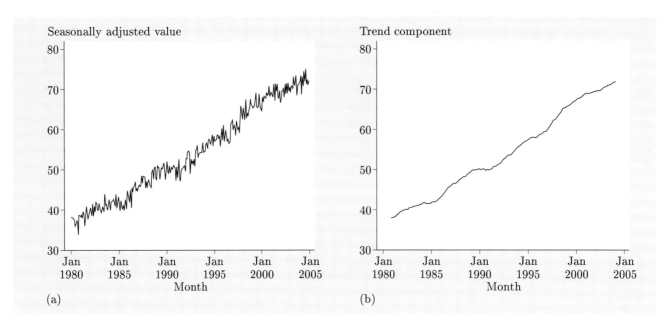

Figure 4.10   Visits overseas: (a) seasonally adjusted series (b) estimated trend component

The seasonally adjusted series z_t retains a trend component and an irregular component, but the seasonal component of the original time series has been removed. The estimated trend component $\widehat{m}_t$ is shown in Figure 4.10(b); this was obtained by smoothing z_t using a simple moving average of order 21.

The irregular component, which is obtained by subtracting the estimated trend component in Figure 4.10(b) from the seasonally adjusted series in Figure 4.10(a), is shown in Figure 4.11.

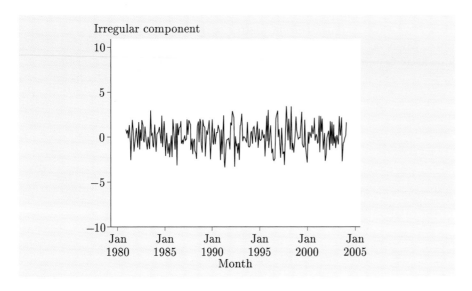

Note that the vertical scale in Figure 4.11 is different from that in Figure 4.10.

Figure 4.11   Visits overseas: irregular component

No trend or seasonality are apparent in the irregular component. All three components of the time series have now been estimated. Adding them together would reproduce the original series exactly.   ♦

Activity 4.5   Seasonally adjusted beer consumption

In Activity 4.4, you estimated the seasonal component of the time series for quarterly beer consumption in the UK. The seasonally adjusted series is shown in Figure 4.12.

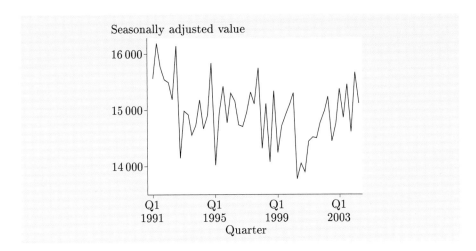

The time plot of the original series was shown in Figure 4.9(a).

Figure 4.12   Beer consumption, seasonally adjusted series

(a) Briefly describe this series.

Two estimates of the trend component are shown in Figure 4.13; these are plotted using the same scale as that used in Figure 4.12.

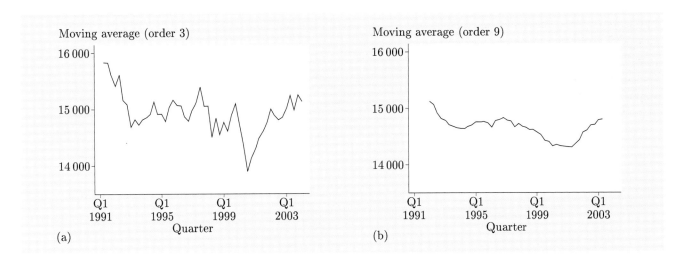

Figure 4.13   Trend component: (a) moving average of order 3 (b) moving average of order 9

(b) Figure 4.13(a) was obtained using a simple moving average of order 3; Figure 4.13(b) was obtained using a simple moving average of order 9. In your opinion, which of the two moving averages results in the better estimate of the trend? Justify your answer.

(c) Summarize the underlying trend in beer consumption.

Summary of Section 4

In this section, you have learned how to estimate the seasonal, trend and irregular components of a time series that can be described by an additive decomposition model. Simple moving averages have been used to estimate the trend component of a non-seasonal time series. Under-smoothing and over-smoothing have been discussed. You have learned how to estimate the seasonal component of a time series using weighted moving averages and how to obtain a seasonally adjusted series. Finally, you have seen how the method for estimating the trend component of a non-seasonal series can be applied to the seasonally adjusted series to obtain estimates of the trend component and the irregular component of the original time series.

Exercises on Section 4

Exercise 4.1   The FTSE100 index

The FTSE100 is an index based on the share prices of 100 leading companies, known as the 'footsie' index. It is one of several such indices used to measure the overall performance of the London stock market. The seasonal variation in the time series of monthly averages is small and may be ignored.

Figure 4.14 shows the time plot of logarithms of the value of the FTSE100 index at the close of trade on the last day of each month between January 1988 and January 2005.

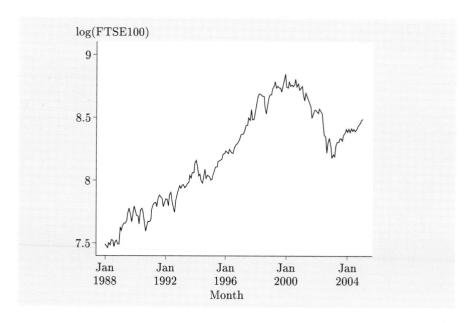

Figure 4.14   Logarithms of the FTSE100 index, 1988–2005

(a) The original data were transformed using logarithms so that an additive model would be appropriate. In your view, has the transformation achieved the desired result? Explain your answer.

The three time plots in Figure 4.15 were obtained by smoothing the time series in Figure 4.14, using simple moving averages of orders 3, 11 and 19.

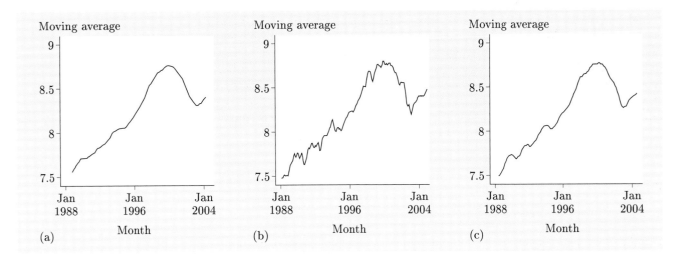

Figure 4.15   Three trend estimates for the log FTSE100 index

(b)   Which moving average was used to produce each of the time plots?

(c)   Discuss which of the three smoothed series in Figure 4.15, if any, gives a good estimate of the trend. If you do not think that any of them provides a good estimate, then suggest another moving average, and explain your choice.

Exercise 4.2   *Temperatures in Recife*

Figure 4.16 contains time plots of the monthly average air temperatures (in degrees Celsius) in Recife, Brazil, from January 1953 to December 1962, and of the seasonally adjusted series.

Chatfield, C. (2004) *The Analysis of Time Series: An Introduction.* Sixth Edition. Chapman & Hall/CRC, London.

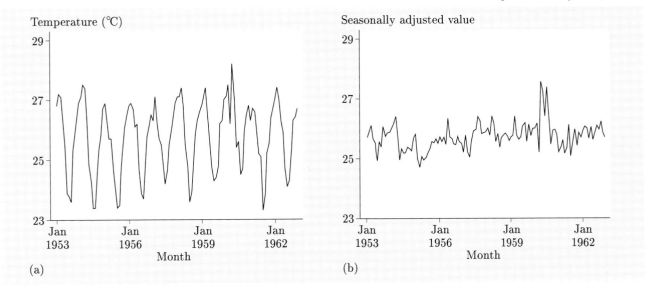

Figure 4.16   Temperatures in Recife: (a) original data (b) seasonally adjusted series

(a)   Briefly describe the two series.

43

(b) The estimated seasonal factors are given in Table 4.4.

Table 4.4   Estimated seasonal factors, $\widehat{s}_j$

Month j	$\widehat{s}_j$
January	1.075
February	1.315
March	0.979
April	0.621
May	−0.158
June	−1.035
July	−1.788
August	−1.800
September	−0.779
October	0.054
November	0.530
December	0.991

Explain briefly how these were obtained from the series shown in Figure 4.16(a), and interpret them. Which is the hottest month in Recife? Which is the coldest month?

Two time plots of the trend component, obtained by smoothing the seasonally adjusted series in Figure 4.16(b), are shown in Figure 4.17.

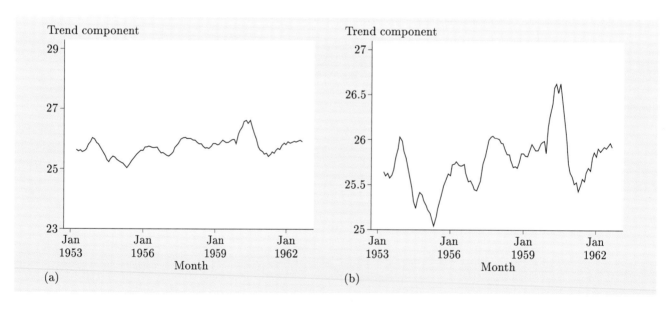

Figure 4.17   Temperatures in Recife: smoothed seasonally adjusted series

(c) Compare the smoothness of the two time series. (*Hint*: look *closely* at how the two plots are drawn.)

(d) Briefly summarize the trend in average temperatures in Recife between 1953 and 1962.

5 Analysing time series in SPSS

In this section, you will learn how to use SPSS to calculate moving averages and to estimate the components of a seasonal time series that can be described by an additive model.

Refer to Chapters 2 and 3 of Computer Book 2 for the work in this section.

Summary of Section 5

In this section, you have learned how to calculate simple moving averages in SPSS, and how to use them to smooth time series. You have also learned how to use SPSS to estimate the seasonal factors of a time series and obtain the seasonally adjusted series. You have used these methods to analyse time series data using the decomposition methods described in Part I.

Part II Forecasting

Introduction to Part II

In Part I, you learned how to use time series data to estimate the components of a time series. The focus of this type of analysis is to describe the *past* features of a time series. Another important use of time series is to use past values to predict *future* values, a process known as **forecasting**.

Forecasting is central to most human activities that involve some degree of forward planning. Weather forecasts are perhaps the most obvious example. Our reliance on pensions, insurance and mortgages also testifies to the importance we place on planning for the future. Good forecasts, and a realistic assessment of the likely reliability of forecasts, can help improve such plans.

Making accurate forecasts is not easy, since forecasting necessarily involves extrapolating beyond the range of the available data: all forecasts are based on the untestable assumption that some aspect of the process that generated the data in the past will also hold for the future. Nevertheless, the quality of forecasts can be improved by using good extrapolation techniques. Some of these techniques are described in Part II.

In Sections 6 and 7, a class of simple yet powerful forecasting methods known collectively as exponential smoothing is described. These methods are commonly used in many fields of application. In Section 8, you will learn how to apply these methods in SPSS. In Section 9, several techniques for evaluating the performance of these forecasting methods are discussed. You will learn how to use SPSS to apply these techniques in Section 10.

6 Exponential smoothing

What will the weather be like next month? What are the chances of an influenza pandemic next year? By how much will the economy grow over the next five years? To answer questions such as these, forecasters have developed complicated models that mimic the underlying processes influencing each outcome, whether they are weather patterns, the spread of infections or economic performance. Complex models are generally required when soundly-based long-term forecasts are needed.

However, in many cases, useful *short-term* forecasts can be obtained by much simpler methods, based on extrapolating historical data. In this section, one such approach, known as **exponential smoothing**, is introduced. In Subsection 6.1, the simplest version of the method is described. This involves a single parameter, whose value has to be chosen by the investigator. Choosing the value of this parameter is the topic of Subsection 6.2.

6.1 Simple exponential smoothing

Example 6.1 will help to set the scene for the exponential smoothing method.

Example 6.1 Predicting tomorrow's temperature

Suppose that it is the evening of 14 August and that today's average temperature was 19.4°C. What will the (average) temperature be tomorrow?

One way to predict tomorrow's average temperature is to assume it will be the same as today's. But was today's temperature typical? A time plot of the average temperatures recorded on recent days should help to answer this question. Figure 6.1 shows the daily average temperatures between 15 July and 14 August.

In fact, these are London temperatures for 15 July to 14 August 2004.

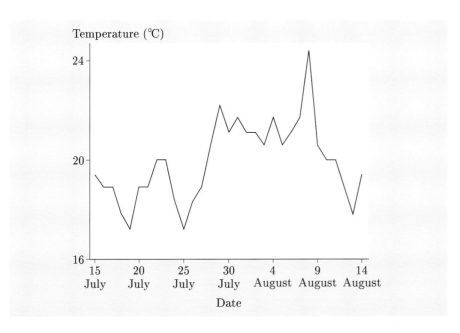

Figure 6.1 Daily average temperatures, 15 July–14 August

Yesterday the average temperature was 17.8°C, and the day before yesterday it was 18.9°C. So perhaps today was unusually hot. A better prediction for tomorrow might be achieved by taking an average of the last three days' values, for example.

However, as you can see from Figure 6.1, the average temperature on each of the last three days was lower than that on any of the previous fifteen days, when the daily average temperature was never below 20.0°C. How should this information affect our prediction for tomorrow?

Clearly, the further back in time we go, the less influence past values should have on our prediction for tomorrow's average temperature; and if we go back too far, seasonal effects would also come into play. But it seems reasonable to predict tomorrow's average temperature by combining past values in some way — for example, by a weighted average in which more weight is given to more recent values. ◆

Suppose that the current time point is $t = n$, and that observations on a time series X_t are available up to time n. Suppose that the time series X_t can be described by an additive model with constant level m and no seasonality. That is, suppose that

$$X_t = m + W_t,$$

where W_t is the irregular component.

The aim is to forecast X_{n+1}, given observations $x_n, x_{n-1}, x_{n-2}, \ldots$. This forecast is called a **1-step ahead forecast of X_{n+1}**, and is denoted $\widehat{x}_{n+1}$. The hat denotes that it is an estimate, and the expression '1-step ahead' emphasizes that the forecast is based on historical data up to and including time n, so that only the *next* value is being forecasted.

As suggested in Example 6.1, a reasonable approach is to use a combination of the present value and past values. There are many possible ways of doing this. The particular combination used in **exponential smoothing** is

$$\widehat{x}_{n+1} = c_0 x_n + c_1 x_{n-1} + c_2 x_{n-2} + c_3 x_{n-3} + \cdots,$$

where

$$c_i = \alpha(1 - \alpha)^i, \quad i = 0, 1, 2, \ldots,$$

and α is a parameter whose value is to be specified, $0 \leq \alpha \leq 1$. That is,

$$\widehat{x}_{n+1} = \alpha x_n + \alpha(1 - \alpha)x_{n-1} + \alpha(1 - \alpha)^2 x_{n-2} + \alpha(1 - \alpha)^3 x_{n-3} + \cdots. \quad (6.1)$$

The c_i are called **exponential weights**. It can be shown that they add up to 1, so $\widehat{x}_{n+1}$, the forecast of X_{n+1}, is a weighted average of the current observation and all past observations. For $0 < \alpha < 1$, the value of c_i decreases as i increases, so greater weight is given to more recent observations. For example, with $\alpha = 0.6$, the forecast of X_{n+1} obtained using (6.1) is

You may recognize the exponential weights as forming a geometric progression.

$$\widehat{x}_{n+1} = 0.6 x_n + 0.6 \times (1 - 0.6)x_{n-1} + 0.6 \times (1 - 0.6)^2 x_{n-2} + \cdots$$
$$= 0.6 x_n + 0.24 x_{n-1} + 0.096 x_{n-2} + \cdots.$$

Thus most weight is given to x_n, followed by x_{n-1}, and so on into the past.

Activity 6.1   Calculating weights

(a) Calculate the weights $c_i = \alpha(1 - \alpha)^i$ for $i = 0, 1, 2, 3, 4$ when $\alpha = 0.5$, and when $\alpha = 0.8$.

(b) Which of these two values of α gives more weight to the current observation?

The dots on the right of the expression for $\widehat{x}_{n+1}$ in (6.1) indicate further terms stretching back into the past. Clearly, it is not possible to carry on indefinitely: it is necessary to stop at some point in the past. But how many terms should be kept? In fact, this problem can be sidestepped, as follows.

Using (6.1) with $n-1$ replacing n throughout, the 1-step ahead forecast of X_n is given by

$$\widehat{x}_n = \alpha x_{n-1} + \alpha(1-\alpha)x_{n-2} + \alpha(1-\alpha)^2 x_{n-3} + \alpha(1-\alpha)^3 x_{n-4} + \cdots.$$

Now note that the expression for $\widehat{x}_{n+1}$ in (6.1) may be rewritten as follows:

$$\begin{aligned}
\widehat{x}_{n+1} &= \alpha x_n + \alpha(1-\alpha)x_{n-1} + \alpha(1-\alpha)^2 x_{n-2} + \alpha(1-\alpha)^3 x_{n-3} + \cdots \\
&= \alpha x_n + (1-\alpha)\left[\alpha x_{n-1} + \alpha(1-\alpha)x_{n-2} + \alpha(1-\alpha)^2 x_{n-3} + \cdots\right]. \quad (6.2)
\end{aligned}$$

But the term in square brackets in (6.2) is $\widehat{x}_n$, so we have

$$\widehat{x}_{n+1} = \alpha x_n + (1-\alpha)\widehat{x}_n. \qquad (6.3)$$

Hence the 1-step ahead forecast of X_{n+1} is a combination of x_n, the observed value of X_n, and $\widehat{x}_n$, the 1-step ahead forecast of X_n. Expression (6.3) makes it possible to obtain a forecast at each time point without having to reach far back into the past. The use of (6.3) is illustrated in Example 6.2.

Example 6.2   *Predicting tomorrow's temperature, continued*

Suppose that today is 14 August and a forecast of the temperature on 15 August is required, based on data on temperatures from 15 July to 14 August. Some of these temperatures are shown in Table 6.1. For convenience, 15 July is labelled $t = 1$, and 14 August is labelled $t = 31$. The parameter value $\alpha = 0.6$ will be used (this choice is arbitrary).

Table 6.1   Observed daily temperatures

Time t	Date	Observed temperature x_t
1	15 July	19.4
2	16 July	18.9
3	17 July	18.9
4	18 July	17.8
⋮	⋮	⋮
29	12 August	18.9
30	13 August	17.8
31	14 August	19.4

The 1-step ahead forecast of X_{32}, the temperature on 15 August, is required; that is, $\widehat{x}_{32}$ is required. To calculate $\widehat{x}_{32}$, the values $\widehat{x}_1, \widehat{x}_2, \ldots, \widehat{x}_{32}$ will be obtained by *iteration*: at each time point t, $\widehat{x}_t$ will be calculated using only the temperatures known prior to that time point.

Iteration means repetition of an operation, or a sequence of operations, at each step using the results of previous steps.

As with all procedures involving iteration, an **initial value** is required. In exponential smoothing, the initial value is often chosen to be the value of the first observation. In this case, the initial value is x_1, the temperature observed on 15 July, so

$$\widehat{x}_1 = x_1 = 19.4.$$

Next, $\widehat{x}_2$, the 1-step ahead forecast of X_2, the temperature on 16 July ($t = 2$), is calculated (as if it were not yet known) using (6.3):

$$\begin{aligned}
\widehat{x}_2 &= 0.6x_1 + 0.4\widehat{x}_1 \\
&= 0.6 \times 19.4 + 0.4 \times 19.4 \\
&= 19.4.
\end{aligned}$$

Then $\widehat{x}_3$, the 1-step ahead forecast of X_3, the (presumed as yet unknown) temperature on 17 July ($t = 3$), is obtained using the observed value $x_2 = 18.9$ and the calculated value $\widehat{x}_2 = 19.4$ in (6.3):

$$\begin{aligned}
\widehat{x}_3 &= 0.6x_2 + 0.4\widehat{x}_2 \\
&= 0.6 \times 18.9 + 0.4 \times 19.4 \\
&= 19.1.
\end{aligned}$$

Similarly, using (6.3) to calculate $\widehat{x}_4$ gives $\widehat{x}_4 = 18.98$. Continuing in this way, using (6.3) repeatedly, leads to a value for $\widehat{x}_{32}$, the 1-step ahead forecast of the temperature on 15 August. Figure 6.2 shows the time series of observed and forecasted temperatures up to 14 August.

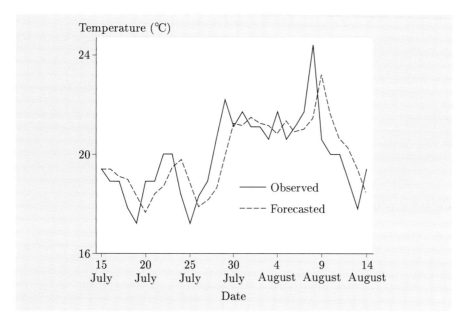

Figure 6.2   Observed temperatures and 1-step ahead forecasts   ♦

In large data sets, calculations such as these are done using a computer. Nevertheless, it is important to understand the principle. Activity 6.2 will give you some practice in applying the method.

Activity 6.2   *Predicting tomorrow's temperature*

Continuing the procedure described in Example 6.2 gives the value $\widehat{x}_{29} \simeq 20.263\,12$. (Note that it is important to keep full accuracy in intermediate calculations.)

(a) Using the data in Table 6.1, obtain the values of $\widehat{x}_{30}$, $\widehat{x}_{31}$ and $\widehat{x}_{32}$.

(b) Summarize your results, stating the forecast for the temperature on 15 August to one decimal place.

As you can see in Figure 6.2, the forecasts track the observed values, and the time plot of forecasts is generally smoother (that is, less spiky) than that of the observed data. The extent of the smoothing depends on the value chosen for the parameter α. Note also that the forecasts show the same general pattern as the data, but with a slight delay.

The method that has been described is called **simple exponential smoothing**. The term *exponential* refers to the fact that the weights $\alpha(1 - \alpha)^i$ lie on an exponential curve. The method is called *simple* because there are more complicated versions of exponential smoothing that can be used for time series with trend and seasonality. These are discussed in Section 7.

The method described in this subsection is summarized in the following box.

Simple exponential smoothing

If a time series X_t is described by an additive model with constant level and no seasonality, 1-step ahead forecasts may be obtained by **simple exponential smoothing** using the formula

$$\widehat{x}_{n+1} = \alpha x_n + (1 - \alpha)\widehat{x}_n,$$

where x_n is the observed value at time n, $\widehat{x}_n$ and $\widehat{x}_{n+1}$ are the 1-step ahead forecasts of X_n and X_{n+1}, and α is a **smoothing parameter**, $0 \le \alpha \le 1$. The method requires an **initial value** $\widehat{x}_1$, which is often chosen to be x_1:

$$\widehat{x}_1 = x_1.$$

6.2   Choosing the smoothing parameter

The simple exponential smoothing method described in Subsection 6.1 involves a smoothing parameter α, $0 \le \alpha \le 1$. Recall that the forecasts are obtained using the formula

$$\widehat{x}_{n+1} = \alpha x_n + (1 - \alpha)\widehat{x}_n.$$

If $\alpha = 1$, then $\widehat{x}_{n+1} = x_n$, so the 1-step ahead forecast is just the current value. A value of α close to 1 means that much weight is placed on the most recent observation, and less weight on observations in the more distant past. The higher the value of α, the more jagged (that is, the less smooth) the time series of forecasts will be, as the forecasts adjust to changes in recent values.

Conversely, for a value of α close to 0, more weight is placed on the distant past than for a value of α close to 1, and less weight on recent observations. The lower the value of α, the smoother the forecasts will be, as they are not affected much by recent values. If $\alpha = 0$, then $\widehat{x}_{n+1} = \widehat{x}_n = \cdots = \widehat{x}_1 = x_1$, the initial value. In this case, the forecasts lie on a horizontal line: the forecasts are all the same, as no weight is given to any observation after the first.

The smoothing effect associated with different choices of α is similar to that obtained when varying the order of a moving average, as described in Section 4.

Example 6.3   *Annual precipitation in England and Wales*

Precipitation includes any water that falls from the sky as rain, sleet, snow or hail, and is measure in millimetres (mm). Figure 6.3 (overleaf) shows the time series of annual precipitation for England and Wales, from 1766 to 2004.

These data were obtained in February 2005 from the website of the Met Office's Hadley Centre http://www.met-office.gov.uk.

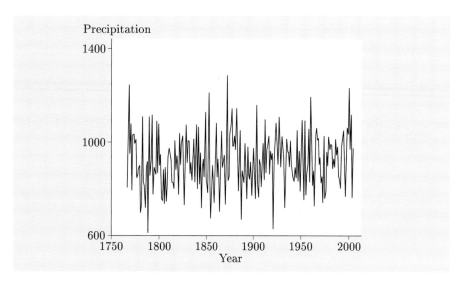

Figure 6.3   Annual precipitation (mm) in England and Wales

Since these are annual data, the series is non-seasonal. There is no clear upward or downward trend over time, and the size of the irregular fluctuations appears to be constant. Thus simple exponential smoothing can be used to obtain forecasts for the years after 2004.

Figure 6.4 shows two sets of 1-step ahead forecasts that were obtained using simple exponential smoothing, as described in Example 6.2, with two different values of the smoothing parameter α.

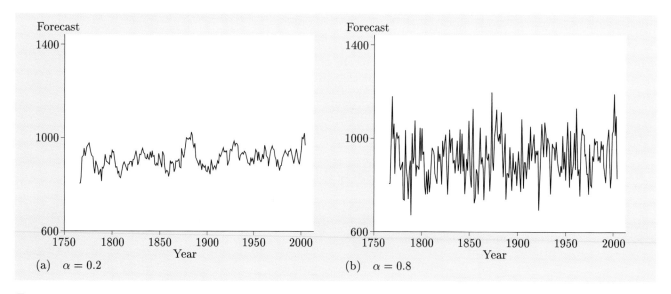

(a) $\alpha = 0.2$ (b) $\alpha = 0.8$

Figure 6.4   Two sets of forecasts for annual precipitation

The value $\alpha = 0.2$ was used to obtain the 1-step ahead forecasts shown in Figure 6.4(a). Little weight is placed on the current year's value, and the resulting forecasts are much less variable than the original time series. The value $\alpha = 0.8$ was used to obtain the 1-step ahead forecasts in Figure 6.4(b). More weight is placed on the current year's value, and the resulting time series of forecasts is much spikier than the series of forecasts obtained using $\alpha = 0.2$.   ◆

As you saw in Example 6.3, different values of α produce different forecasts. So how should the value of α be chosen? There are two approaches. The first is to rely on past experience with other, similar, series: if some value of α has been shown to produce accurate forecasts, then that value is used. The second approach, which will be described here, is to estimate α from past data. The idea is to choose the value of α which, if applied to the data available, would have produced the most accurate forecasts. But first, a way to assess the accuracy of forecasts is needed. A method is described in Example 6.4.

Example 6.4   *Assessing the accuracy of forecasts*

In Example 6.2, temperature forecasts were obtained for each day from 15 July to 14 August using $\alpha = 0.6$. These forecasts are shown in Table 6.2, together with the temperatures actually observed.

Table 6.2   Forecasted and observed temperatures

Time t and date	Forecast temperature $\widehat{x}_t$	Observed temperature x_t	Forecast error $x_t - \widehat{x}_t$
1 15 July	19.400	19.4	0.000
2 16 July	19.400	18.9	−0.500
3 17 July	19.100	18.9	−0.200
4 18 July	18.980	17.8	−1.180
⋮	⋮	⋮	⋮
29 12 August	20.263	18.9	−1.363
30 13 August	19.445	17.8	−1.645
31 14 August	18.458	19.4	0.942

The accuracy of the forecast for each day can be assessed by the difference between the observed value and the forecast. This difference is called the *forecast error* and is denoted e_t. The forecast errors are shown in the fourth column of Table 6.2. The first value is zero because the initial value was chosen to be the temperature actually observed on the first day.

A convenient way of summarizing the overall accuracy of the forecasts by a single number is to add up the squares of the forecast errors:

$$(0)^2 + (-0.500)^2 + (-0.200)^2 + (-1.180)^2 + \cdots + (-1.363)^2$$
$$+ (-1.645)^2 + (0.942)^2 = 49.223.$$

This number is called the *sum of squared errors*; it is often abbreviated to *SSE*. Thus, in this example, the sum of squared errors is 49.223.   ◆

In Example 6.4, the 1-step ahead **forecast error** at time t (which is also called the **error**, or the **residual**, at time t) was defined to be the difference between x_t, the value observed at time t, and $\widehat{x}_t$, the 1-step ahead forecast of X_t. The overall accuracy of the forecasts may be assessed by the **sum of squared errors**, or **SSE**.

If the forecast errors are large, they will produce a large value of the *SSE*. Thus lower values of the *SSE* should correspond to better forecasts. A natural way to choose the value of the parameter α is to choose the value which minimizes the *SSE*. This value of α is said to be **optimal**. The procedure is summarized in the following box.

Forecast errors and choice of smoothing parameter

The 1-step ahead **forecast error** at time t, which is denoted e_t, is the difference between the observed value and the 1-step ahead forecast of X_t:

$$e_t = x_t - \widehat{x}_t.$$

The **sum of squared errors**, or **SSE**, is given by

$$SSE = \sum_{t=1}^{n} e_t^2 = \sum_{t=1}^{n} (x_t - \widehat{x}_t)^2 .$$

Given observed values $x_1, x_2, \ldots, x_n$, the **optimal** value of the smoothing parameter α for simple exponential smoothing is the value that minimizes the sum of squared errors.

Example 6.5 illustrates the optimal choice of smoothing parameter.

Example 6.5   Optimal choice of smoothing parameter

For the summer temperature data that were introduced in Example 6.1, values of the SSE were obtained for several different values of α. These are shown in Table 6.3.

Table 6.3   Values of SSE for different α

Smoothing parameter α	SSE	Forecast for 15 August
0	86.19	19.40
0.1	71.64	20.15
0.2	63.00	19.87
0.3	57.17	19.48
0.4	53.37	19.21
0.5	50.87	19.07
0.6	49.22	19.02
0.7	48.26	19.05
0.8	47.95	19.13
0.9	48.29	19.25
1	49.32	19.40

The SSE is smallest for $\alpha = 0.8$. With this value of α, the forecasted temperature for 15 August is 19.13°C. The high value of α means that much weight is placed on recent observations.   ◆

Activity 6.3   Forecasting annual precipitation

Table 6.4 shows, for different values of α, the value of the SSE and the forecasted precipitation for 2005, based on the data for 1766 to 2004.

Table 6.4 SSE and forecasted precipitation for 2005

Smoothing parameter α	SSE	Forecast for 2005 (mm)
0	6 242 680	805.5
0.01	3 916 676	913.0
0.02	3 648 339	929.7
0.05	3 563 853	944.5
0.1	3 602 603	959.1
0.2	3 746 147	970.1
0.3	3 946 979	966.6
0.4	4 192 445	957.0
0.5	4 478 857	947.1
0.6	4 809 321	940.7
0.7	5 191 416	939.6
0.8	5 636 379	944.6
0.9	6 159 532	955.8
1	6 781 865	973.6

(a)   Identify the optimal value of the smoothing parameter α, and give the corresponding forecasted precipitation for 2005 based on data for 1766 to 2004.

(b)   Interpret the optimal value of α in terms of the weight accorded to recent and distant past observations.

Summary of Section 6

In this section, the simple exponential smoothing method for forecasting time series with constant level and no seasonality has been described. This method involves iteration with the initial value chosen to be equal to the first observed value of the time series. You have learned how to calculate and interpret 1-step ahead forecasts. The effect of using different values for the smoothing parameter has been illustrated. Forecast errors have been defined, and the method of choosing the value of the smoothing parameter by minimizing the sum of squared errors has been described.

Exercises on Section 6

Exercise 6.1   Calculating forecasts

In Activity 4.2, data on successive two-hourly readings on the concentration of a chemical process were described. Table 6.5 shows the first four readings, taken at times 2, 4, 6 and 8 hours.

(a) Obtain the 1-step ahead forecast for the concentration at 10 hours using simple exponential smoothing, with initial value $\widehat{x}_1 = x_1$ and smoothing parameter $\alpha = 0.2$.

(b) Calculate the SSE to three decimal places.

Table 6.5   Chemical concentrations

t	Time	Concentration
1	2 hours	17.0
2	4 hours	16.6
3	6 hours	16.3
4	8 hours	16.1

Exercise 6.2   Choosing the smoothing parameter

The time series used in Exercise 6.1 comprises 197 successive two-hourly readings, taken at times 2 to 394 hours. Simple exponential smoothing was used with these data to predict the concentration at 396 hours (time point 198) for several values of the smoothing parameter α. Table 6.6 shows the SSE and the forecast $\widehat{x}_{198}$ for each of these values of α.

(a) Identify the optimal value of α among those listed in Table 6.6, and explain your choice. Hence write down the corresponding forecast for X_{198}.

(b) Suppose that the value of the smoothing parameter is chosen to be 0.8. Will the time series of forecasts be smoother than that obtained using the optimal value of α you identified in part (a), or will it be less smooth? Explain your answer.

Table 6.6 SSE and forecasted concentration

Smoothing parameter α	SSE	Forecast at 396 hours
0	32.01	17.00
0.1	21.83	17.45
0.2	20.17	17.51
0.3	19.89	17.50
0.4	20.07	17.47
0.5	20.52	17.43
0.6	21.19	17.41
0.7	22.09	17.39
0.8	23.26	17.38
0.9	24.79	17.39
1	26.74	17.40

7 Holt–Winters forecasting

The simple exponential smoothing method can be used for time series with constant level and no seasonality. In this section, more general exponential smoothing methods are presented. In Subsection 7.1, an extension of simple exponential smoothing which is appropriate for time series with a linear trend is described. In Subsection 7.2, this is extended further to time series with a seasonal component. A note of caution about forecasting in general is given in Subsection 7.3.

7.1 Holt's exponential smoothing method

The simple exponential smoothing method described in Section 6 applies to additive time series with constant level and no seasonality, which can be described by the model

$$X_t = m + W_t.$$

The parameter m is the level (or mean) of the series, and W_t is the irregular component (with mean zero). What happens if simple exponential smoothing is used on a time series with a trend component that is not constant? This is illustrated in Example 7.1.

Example 7.1 Annual average house prices

Figure 7.1 shows the time plot of annual average house prices in the UK from 1996 to 2004, and the forecasts obtained using simple exponential smoothing.

These data were obtained in February 2005 from the website of the Nationwide Building Society www.nationwide.co.uk/hpi.

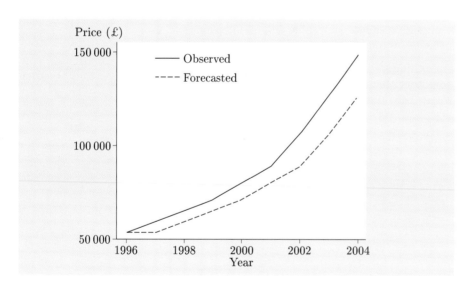

Figure 7.1   Observed and forecasted average house prices, 1996–2004

The optimal value of the smoothing parameter for this time series is $\alpha = 1$. In this case, (6.3) reduces to

$$\widehat{x}_{t+1} = x_t,$$

Other values of α all give forecasts lower than the current value.

so the forecast at each time point is the current value. Since there is an increasing trend, the forecast always lags behind the observed value. For example, in 2003 the average house price was £126 840. Hence the forecast for 2004 was also £126 840, whereas the actual average 2004 observed price was £148 548.   ◆

The simple exponential smoothing forecast $\widehat{x}_{t+1}$ is an estimate of m_t, the level of the time series at time t, that is, at the *preceding* time point. When the level is constant, so that $m_{t+1} = m_t = m$, this is not a problem: in this case, the method gives accurate forecasts. However, when there is a rising trend (as in Example 7.1) or a declining trend, the method can produce inaccurate forecasts.

Suppose that the time series X_t can be described by an additive non-seasonal model with a linear trend component, that is,

$$X_t = m + bt + W_t,$$

where b is the slope of the trend component $m_t = m + bt$. Note that

$$\begin{aligned}
X_{t+1} &= m + b(t+1) + W_{t+1} \\
&= (m + bt) + b + W_{t+1} \\
&= m_t + b + W_{t+1}.
\end{aligned} \tag{7.1}$$

The 1-step ahead forecast for X_{t+1} obtained using simple exponential smoothing is an estimate of m_t, the level at time t, so that

$$\widehat{x}_{t+1} = \widehat{m}_t.$$

From expression (7.1), since W_{t+1} has mean zero, the expected value of X_{t+1} is $m_t + b$. Hence a better forecast is

$$\widehat{x}_{t+1} = \widehat{m}_t + \widehat{b},$$

where $\widehat{b}$ is an estimate of the slope. In Example 7.1, this would mean 'adding a bit on' to this year's estimate, in line with recent growth in house prices.

Holt's exponential smoothing method provides a way of estimating both the level m_t and the slope b at each time point. This is achieved by a smoothing method very similar to that used in simple exponential smoothing. The main difference between Holt's method and simple exponential smoothing is that the smoothing is now controlled by two parameters — one parameter α for the estimate of the level m_t at the current time point, and one parameter γ for the estimate of the slope b. The values of both parameters, α and γ, lie between 0 and 1. As with simple exponential smoothing, values of the parameters close to 0 mean that little weight is placed on the most recent observations. On the other hand, values close to 1 mean that much weight is placed on the most recent observations.

The details are omitted. You will use SPSS to do the calculations in Section 8.

The symbol γ is the Greek lower-case letter gamma.

Example 7.2   Annual average house prices: Holt's method

Figure 7.2 shows the observed average house prices and the forecasted values obtained using Holt's exponential smoothing method.

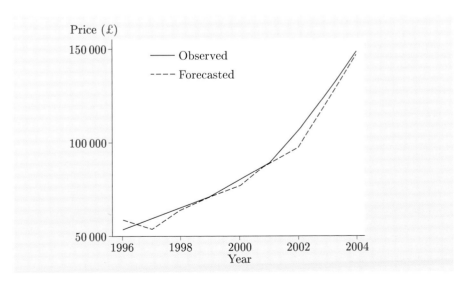

Figure 7.2   Observed and forecasted values using Holt's method

Notice that the forecasts obtained using Holt's exponential smoothing method are much more accurate than those obtained using simple exponential smoothing (which are shown in Figure 7.1). ◆

57

To implement Holt's method, two initial values are needed — an initial value for the level, and an initial value for the slope. The initial value for the level is taken to be x_1, as for simple exponential smoothing. There are several possibilities for the initial value for the slope, including $x_2 - x_1$, the difference between the first two observations, and 0, which is a sensible choice when the slope is not clear. In Example 7.2, the initial value for the slope parameter was the difference $x_2 - x_1$.

The sum of squared errors SSE is defined in exactly the same way as for simple exponential smoothing:

$$SSE = \sum_{t=1}^{n} \left(x_t - \widehat{x}_t \right)^2.$$

The values of the smoothing parameters α and γ are chosen so that the SSE is minimized. The forecasts in Figure 7.2 were obtained using these optimal values: $\alpha = 0.94$ and $\gamma = 1$. Thus the most recent values of the level and the slope are given much weight. A further illustration of the method is given in Example 7.3.

Example 7.3   Central England temperatures, 1901–2004

Suppose that we wish to forecast the average temperature in 2005 in Central England, using the annual average temperatures for Central England from 1901 to 2004. The first step is to obtain the time plot of the data. This is shown in Figure 7.3.

This data set is a subset of the data set described in Example 1.2.

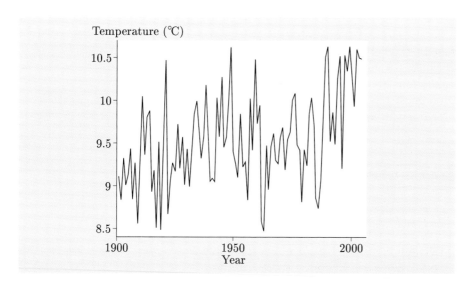

Figure 7.3   Annual average Central England temperatures (°C), 1901–2004

The data are annual, so the time series is not seasonal, and the width of the irregular fluctuations does not appear to vary with the level. Temperatures appear higher towards the end of the series than at the beginning, so it is not unreasonable to assume that there might be an increasing trend. Thus Holt's exponential smoothing method can be used to obtain 1-step ahead forecasts, and in particular the forecast for 2005.

The 1901 temperature was 9.11°C, so the initial value for the level is $x_1 = 9.11$. For an initial value for the slope, the difference between the first two values could be used: in this case, $x_2 - x_1 = 8.83 - 9.11 = -0.28$. Alternatively, 0 could be used as the initial value. Since the trend is not obvious, but is unlikely to be downward, 0 seems more appropriate here than -0.28.

The values of the smoothing parameters α and γ that give the smallest value of the SSE are (to two decimal places) $\alpha = 0.05$ and $\gamma = 0.36$. Thus the level depends very little on recent values, and the slope a little more so.

The 1-step ahead forecasts for the period 1901 to 2005 are shown in Figure 7.4.

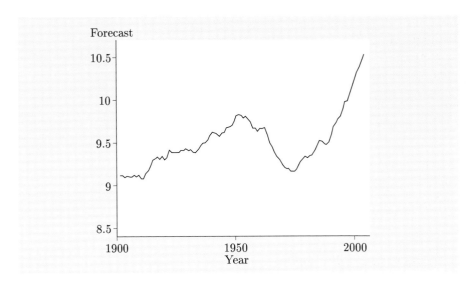

Figure 7.4   1-step ahead forecasts for annual average temperatures (°C), 1901–2005

The time series of forecasts is quite smooth: this is because the value of α is close to zero. For Holt's method with optimal parameter values, the SSE is 25.32. The forecasted average temperature for 2005 is 10.59°C.

What would have happened if the simple exponential smoothing method had been used with these data? For simple exponential smoothing, the optimal value of α is 0.15 in this case, the SSE is 25.64, and the forecasted temperature is 10.24°C. Thus the SSE is slightly higher and the forecasted temperature slightly lower than with Holt's method. In this example, Holt's method is only marginally preferable (owing to the smaller SSE) to the simple exponential smoothing method.   ◆

In Example 7.3, Holt's method provided only a marginal improvement over simple exponential smoothing. This illustrates a useful property of all exponential smoothing methods: they are quite **robust**. In other words, *moderate* departure from the assumptions does not generally have a large adverse effect on the accuracy of the forecasts. In Example 7.1, the level of the time series is clearly not constant, so the departure from the assumption of constant level was decidedly *not* moderate: simple exponential smoothing gave inaccurate forecasts in that example.

Activity 7.1 will give you some practice at interpreting the forecasts obtained using Holt's exponential smoothing method.

Activity 7.1   Forecasting house prices

Examples 7.1 and 7.2 used annual house price data. This activity is based on the monthly time series of average house prices, expressed in pounds sterling, in England between January 1991 and January 2005. In this activity, you will discuss forecasts of average house prices for February 2005, obtained by applying Holt's exponential smoothing to the logarithms of monthly average house prices between January 1996 and January 2005. The log transformation is used so that the monthly time series may be described using an additive model.

This time series was introduced in Example 1.4.

59

The time plot of the natural logarithms of average house prices is shown in Figure 7.5.

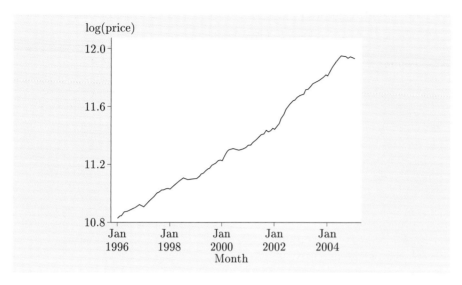

Figure 7.5   Logarithms of average house prices, January 1996 to January 2005

The first two values of the time series are 10.830 13 in January 1996, and 10.844 58 in February 1996.

(a) Why is Holt's exponential smoothing to be preferred over simple exponential smoothing for this time series?

(b) Suggest appropriate initial values for the level and the slope.

(c) Table 7.1 shows the values of the SSE obtained for several pairs of values of the parameters α and γ, and the corresponding forecasts for February 2005. Identify the optimal combination of parameter values, and obtain the forecasted average house price in pounds sterling for February 2005, to the nearest £100.

Figure 7.6 shows the observed values and the 1-step ahead forecasts for the year leading up to February 2005, expressed on the original scale (pounds sterling).

Table 7.1   Parameters, SSE and forecasts

α	γ	SSE	Forecast
0.8	0.1	0.012 72	11.9412
0.8	0.3	0.011 80	11.9312
0.8	0.5	0.011 05	11.9277
1	0.1	0.010 75	11.9373
1	0.3	0.010 47	11.9294
1	0.5	0.010 72	11.9265

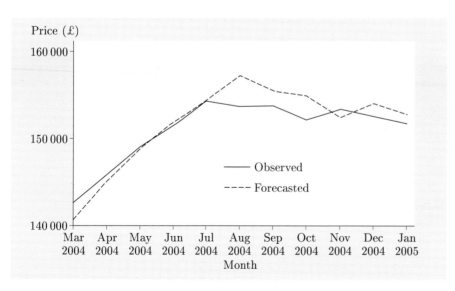

Figure 7.6   Observed and forecasted average house prices, March 2004 to January 2005

(d) The upward trend in house prices ended in August 2004. Briefly describe how the forecasts adjusted to this change.

7.2 Holt–Winters exponential smoothing

Holt's exponential smoothing method applies only to non-seasonal time series. A further extension of exponential smoothing, that includes both a linear trend component and seasonality, is known as **Holt–Winters exponential smoothing**. This method is appropriate for time series that can be described by an additive model with a linear trend component $m + bt$ and a seasonal component s_t, that is,

$$X_t = m + bt + s_t + W_t.$$

A version of the Holt–Winters method exists for multiplicative models, but this will not be discussed in this book.

Using the Holt–Winters method, the 1-step ahead forecast of X_{t+1} is

$$\widehat{x}_{t+1} = \widehat{m}_t + \widehat{b} + \widehat{s}_{t+1}.$$

This method involves three smoothing parameters. In addition to the two parameters for Holt's exponential smoothing method (α for the level and γ for the slope), there is a third smoothing parameter, δ. This parameter adjusts the estimate of the seasonal component. Optimal values of the three parameters α, γ and δ may be chosen by minimizing the SSE. For all three parameters, values close to 1 indicate that much weight is placed on the most recent observations, and values close to 0 indicate that little weight is placed on the most recent observations.

The symbol δ is the Greek lower-case letter delta.

There are many different ways of choosing initial values. For simplicity, x_1 will generally be used as the initial value for the level, and either 0 or $(x_{T+1} - x_1)/T$ as the initial value for the slope, where T is the period of the seasonal component. Initial values for the seasonal factors can be obtained by estimating the seasonal components using the method described in Subsection 4.2.

Example 7.4 Forecasting house prices

In Activity 7.1, the application of Holt's exponential smoothing method to the time series of logarithms of average house prices was discussed. In fact, house prices are seasonal (see Figure 1.8(b)). Therefore the Holt–Winters method is more appropriate.

The initial values will be chosen as follows. The initial value for the level is the first value of the series, namely $x_1 = 10.830\,13$. This value corresponds to January 1996. Since the period of the seasonal component is 12, the initial value for the slope is the difference between the first two January values, divided by 12:

$$(x_{13} - x_1)/12 = (10.908\,81 - 10.830\,13)/12 \simeq 0.0066.$$

The initial values for the seasonal factors were derived using the method described in Subsection 4.2 for estimating the seasonal factors of a time series. Using these initial values, the optimal parameter values were $\alpha = 0.9$, $\gamma = 0.3$ and $\delta = 0.0$. The fact that the estimate of the parameter δ was 0 means that the initial values for the seasonal factors did not need to be updated; it does *not* mean that the seasonal component was not required in the model.

In this book, you will not need to supply starting values for the seasonal factors: these are calculated by the course software.

For the Holt–Winters forecasting method with the optimal parameter values, the SSE is 0.006 22, compared to 0.010 47 for Holt's method. Thus the Holt–Winters method gives better forecasts, as would be expected since the time series is seasonal.

Figure 7.7 (overleaf) shows the forecasts for the year leading up to February 2005, on the original scale; these were obtained by taking exponentials.

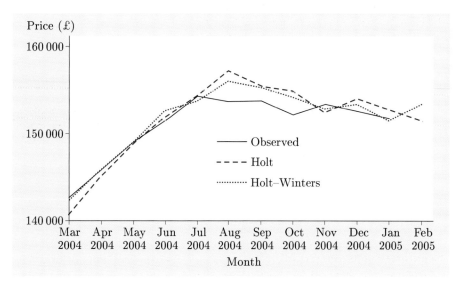

Figure 7.7   House prices: observed value, Holt forecast and Holt–Winters forecast

It appears that the Holt–Winters forecasts responded slightly more rapidly than the Holt forecasts to the change in the slope of the trend in August 2004.   ◆

Activity 7.2 provides a further comparison of the three exponential smoothing methods described in Sections 6 and 7.

Activity 7.2   *Forecasting monthly temperatures*

The time plot of monthly average temperatures in Central England from January 1970 to December 2004 is shown in Figure 7.8(a).

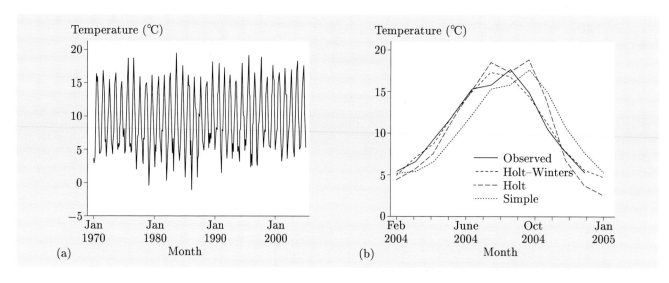

Figure 7.8   Central England temperatures: (a) time plot, 1970–2004 (b) observed values and forecasts, February 2004 to January 2005

Figure 7.8(b) shows the 1-step ahead forecasts for the year up to January 2005 obtained by using the simple, Holt and Holt–Winters exponential smoothing methods.

(a)   The *SSE*s for the three methods are 3387, 799 and 3300 (not necessarily in that order). Which *SSE* corresponds to the Holt–Winters model, and why?

(b) The forecasted monthly temperatures for February 2005 were 5.3°C using simple exponential smoothing, 2.6°C using Holt's method, and 4.8°C using the Holt–Winters method. Which forecast is likely to be the most reliable? Briefly justify your answer.

The Holt–Winters exponential smoothing method allows for both a linear trend and seasonality. Occasionally, there is no trend, just seasonal variation around a broadly constant level. In this case, the smoothing parameter γ for the slope is omitted, and the resulting method is known as **Winters exponential smoothing**. This method will not be discussed further in this book.

> Several other exponential smoothing methods exist, but are not covered in this book.

7.3   A note of caution

All forecasting methods based on time series data are based on the assumption that the past is a useful guide to the future, and hence that the values observed in the past can be used to predict those that will arise in the future. This assumption is very much an act of faith. Furthermore, there are plenty of examples to show that it can be wrong. One such example is described in Example 7.5 and Activity 7.3.

Example 7.5   Forecasting the FTSE100 index

The FTSE100 index was described in Exercise 4.1. Changes in the value of the index are used to measure the performance of financial markets.

Figure 7.9 shows the time plot of the FTSE100 index at close of trade on the last day of each month between April 1984 and September 1987, together with the 1-step ahead forecasts produced by Holt's exponential smoothing method.

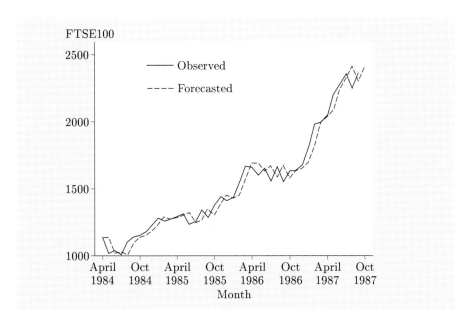

Figure 7.9   FTSE100 index: observed values and forecasts

The optimal values of the smoothing parameters, which were used to obtain the forecasts, were $\alpha = 0.91$ and $\gamma = 0.09$.

The index climbed steadily throughout this period. In line with this performance, the forecast for October 1987 was 2406.94. What happened next is the subject of Activity 7.3. ◆

Activity 7.3   What happened next

The steady upward trend in the FTSE100 index which continued through the mid 1980s reflected a generally confident mood in the world of finance. For example, on 26 August 1987 the *Wall Street Journal* (a leading business newspaper in the USA) quoted a financial expert as saying that 'It's pretty much taken for granted now that the market is going to go up'.

Other voices urged caution, warning that the steady upward trend was unsustainable.

On 19 October 1987 the world's stock markets crashed and share prices dropped sharply. Figure 7.10 shows the FTSE100 index and the forecasts for the period April 1984 to October 1987.

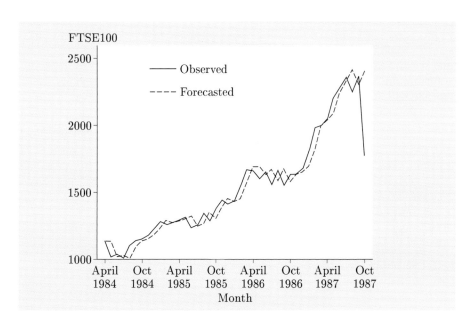

Figure 7.10   The October 1987 stock market crash

The forecast for October 1987 obtained using Holt's method, as described in Example 7.5, was 2406.94 points; the actual value was 1749.80.

(a)   Calculate the forecast error for October 1987. Comment on the accuracy of the forecast for October 1987, compared to the accuracy of forecasts for the months prior to October 1987.

(b)   The forecasts shown in Figure 7.10 were obtained using Holt's exponential smoothing method. Could the accuracy of the forecast for October 1987 have been improved by using the Holt–Winters method? Explain your answer.

Example 7.5 and Activity 7.3 illustrate the important point that achieving a good agreement between observed values and predicted values using past data by minimizing the *SSE* does not guarantee that future predictions will be accurate. In this connection, it is important to distinguish between *in-sample* forecasting errors (for which the *SSE* is minimized) and *out-of-sample* forecasting errors, namely those obtained by applying the method to forecast values that genuinely lie in the future. In general, out-of-sample forecasting errors tend to be larger than in-sample forecasting errors.

No statistical forecasting method could have predicted that share prices would collapse in October 1987 because, in this particular case, the recent past was a very bad guide to what was to happen next. Nevertheless, exceptional events such as this are uncommon. In many contexts, time series are more predictable, and short-term extrapolation methods, including those based on exponential smoothing, provide reliable results — most of the time . . . .

If statisticians were able to predict such events, they would be very rich indeed!

Summary of Section 7

In this section, simple exponential smoothing has been extended to more general settings. You have learned how to obtain 1-step ahead forecasts using Holt's exponential smoothing method for time series with a linear trend. The Holt–Winters method, which applies to seasonal time series with linear trend, has been described. Some of the limitations of statistical forecasting methods have been emphasized.

Exercise on Section 7

Exercise 7.1   Choosing a forecasting method

Figure 7.11 shows the time plots of four time series. You may assume that any cyclic variation in these plots is seasonal.

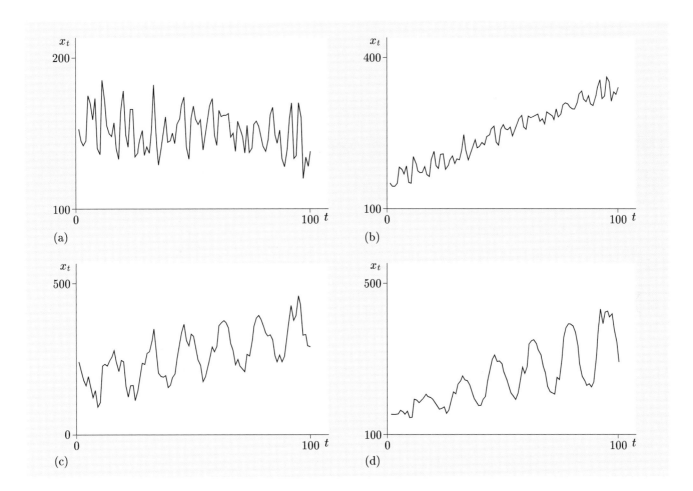

Figure 7.11   Four time series

For each of the time series in Figure 7.11, exponential smoothing is to be used to forecast the next value of the series. For each series, state which of simple exponential smoothing, Holt's exponential smoothing and Holt–Winters exponential smoothing you might use, if any, and which of the methods you would not use. In each case, give your reasons.

65

8 Exponential smoothing in SPSS

In this section, you will learn how to use SPSS to obtain 1-step ahead forecasts using simple exponential smoothing, Holt's method and the Holt–Winters method. You will also learn how to obtain forecasts more than one step ahead.

Refer to Chapters 4 and 5 of Computer Book 2 for the work in this section.

Summary of Section 8

In this section, you have learned how to implement simple, Holt's and Holt–Winters exponential smoothing in SPSS, and how to obtain forecasts using these methods.

9 Autocorrelation and prediction intervals

Two questions are addressed in this section.

◇ Could the forecasting method be improved upon?

◇ How accurate are the forecasts of future values?

Producing a forecast is easy, but producing a *good* forecast is much more difficult. Ultimately, it can only be known for sure if a forecasting method is any good by comparing the forecast with the actual outcome. However, it is also possible, to some limited extent, to assess the reliability of a forecast by studying the statistical properties of the method used to obtain it, and by calculating an estimate of the uncertainty surrounding it.

The key idea in this section is to make use of information about the correlations between successive forecast errors. In Subsection 9.1, these correlations are discussed, and a graphical method for displaying them is presented. In Subsection 9.2, two tests for zero correlation are described. A simple method for assessing the uncertainty of a forecast is described in Subsection 9.3.

9.1 The correlogram

The exponential smoothing methods described in Sections 6 and 7 all involve obtaining 1-step ahead forecasts $\widehat{x}_1, \widehat{x}_2, \ldots, \widehat{x}_n$ of the past values $x_1, x_2, \ldots, x_n$, from which forecast errors $e_t = x_t - \widehat{x}_t$ are calculated. The 1-step ahead forecast errors e_t are observations on random variables E_t, which themselves constitute a time series:

$$E_t = X_t - \widehat{x}_t.$$

Provided that an appropriate forecasting method was chosen, the forecast errors should not display any trend or seasonality. They should fluctuate around zero, with roughly constant variance.

In this subsection, the *correlations* between the forecast errors are investigated. If the correlation between E_{t-1} and E_t, say, or between E_{t-2} and E_t, is non-zero, then it should be possible to improve upon the forecasting method. This idea is developed in Example 9.1.

Correlation is discussed in the *Introduction to statistical modelling*.

Example 9.1   British Government securities

Figure 9.1(a) shows the time plot for the monthly percentage yields on British Government securities, for 21 years between 1950 and 1970. (For definiteness, the time span January 1950 to December 1970 has been used.)

Chatfield, C. (2004) *The Analysis of Time Series: An Introduction.* Sixth Edition. Chapman & Hall/CRC, London.

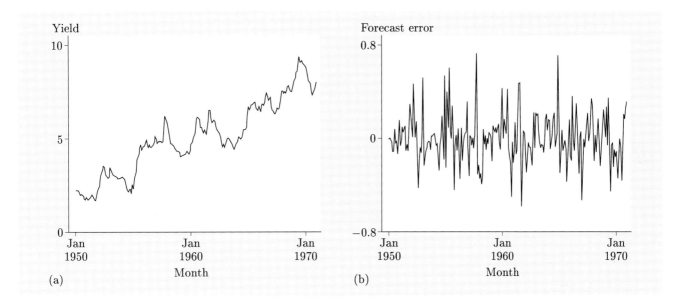

Figure 9.1   Percentage yields on Government securities: (a) time plot (b) forecast errors

Analysis of the time series suggested that there is no substantial seasonal variation, so Holt's exponential smoothing method was used to obtain 1-step ahead forecasts. The forecast errors are shown in Figure 9.1(b). The errors appear to be distributed around zero, with constant variance. But are the errors correlated?

Suppose, for example, that the correlation between E_{t-1} and E_t is positive. Then a large positive forecast error will tend to be followed by another large positive forecast error, and a large negative forecast error by another large negative error. The correlation between the forecast errors can be investigated by arranging the forecast errors in pairs (e_{t-1}, e_t) and calculating the correlation coefficient for these pairs. There are $n = 252$ time points, so there are 251 pairs: $(e_1, e_2), (e_2, e_3), \ldots, (e_{251}, e_{252})$. The sample correlation coefficient is 0.34, which suggests a weak positive correlation.

Is E_{t-2} correlated with E_t? To investigate this, the sample correlation coefficient can be calculated from the 250 pairs $(e_1, e_3), (e_2, e_4), \ldots, (e_{250}, e_{252})$. The correlation coefficient is 0.045, which is close to zero, suggesting that there is no correlation.

These correlations may also be conveyed graphically. Figure 9.2(a) shows a scatterplot of the pairs $(e_1, e_2), (e_2, e_3), \ldots, (e_{251}, e_{252})$.

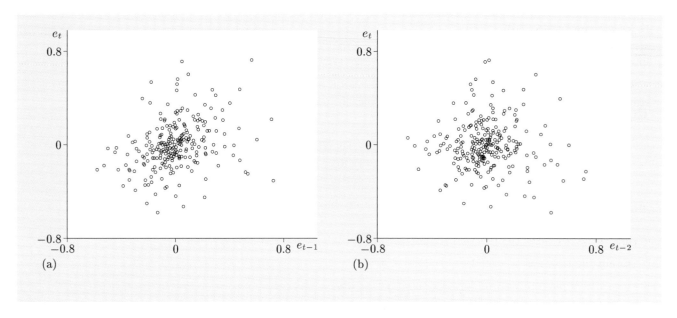

Figure 9.2 Scatterplots of forecast errors: (a) e_t and e_{t-1} (b) e_t and e_{t-2}

Figure 9.2(b) shows a scatterplot of the pairs $(e_1, e_3), (e_2, e_4), \ldots, (e_{250}, e_{252})$. The points in the scatterplot in Figure 9.2(a) lie around a line with positive slope, so this suggests that the correlation between E_t and E_{t-1} is positive. On the other hand, the scatterplot in Figure 9.2(b) suggests there is little if any correlation between E_t and E_{t-2}.

The existence of a positive correlation between the random variables E_{t-1} and E_t has the following practical consequence. Suppose that the value x_{n-1} has been observed at time $n - 1$, and that the 1-step ahead forecast $\widehat{x}_n$ has been obtained. This is a forecast of X_n, the value at time n. The forecast error at time $n - 1$ is $e_{n-1} = x_{n-1} - \widehat{x}_{n-1}$. Suppose that this is large and positive. Since the correlation between one forecast error and the next is positive, we might expect that $E_n = X_n - \widehat{x}_n$ will also turn out to be large and positive. In this case, it would be sensible to increase the forecast $\widehat{x}_n$ a little, so as to reduce the likely forecast error. Thus knowledge of the correlation suggests a way of improving the forecast. In other words, the forecast method that has been used is not the best possible, since a way has been found of improving upon it.   ♦

In Example 9.1, the sample correlation was calculated using the pairs $(e_1, e_2), (e_2, e_3), \ldots, (e_{251}, e_{252})$. One way to think of this is as follows. Start with the original time series $e_1, e_2, \ldots, e_{252}$ and shift it along one place, removing the last observation. This gives the time series $*, e_1, e_2, \ldots, e_{251}$, where the star denotes an empty position. The original time series is said to have been **lagged by one place**. The correlation is then calculated between the original time series and the lagged time series, ignoring the values in the first position. This is the correlation at lag one, the **lag** being the number of places the time series has been shifted.

Similarly, the correlation at lag 3, for example, would be calculated between the time series $e_1, e_2, e_3, \ldots, e_{252}$ and the time series $*, *, *, e_1, e_2, \ldots, e_{249}$, ignoring the first three values.

Since these correlation coefficients are calculated between the original time series and lagged versions of the same time series, they are called sample **autocorrelations**. The formula for calculating a sample autocorrelation is very similar (but not identical) to that used for calculating the sample Pearson correlation coefficient, and it gives virtually identical results in large samples.

The algebraic expression for calculating the sample autocorrelation has been omitted as you will not be required to calculate any autocorrelations by hand.

Sample autocorrelations are defined in the following box.

Sample autocorrelation at lag k

If X_t is a time series with n observed values $x_1, x_2, \ldots, x_n$, then the time series **lagged by k places** is the time series with X_{t-k} in position t. The first k positions of the lagged series comprise missing values.

The **sample autocorrelation at lag k** is a correlation coefficient r_k calculated between a time series and a copy of itself, lagged by k places; it is calculated using the $n - k$ pairs of points
$(x_1, x_{k+1}), (x_2, x_{k+2}), \ldots, (x_{n-k}, x_n)$.

Activity 9.1   *Lagged time series and autocorrelations*

The time series X_t takes the ten values 5, 1, 4, −9, 3, −3, 7, 0, −1, 8.

(a) Obtain the time series lagged by five places.

(b) From which pairs of values are the sample autocorrelations r_3 and r_6 calculated?

(c) In any time series, the autocorrelation at lag 0 is equal to 1. Explain why this is so.

In a time series with n values, it is possible to calculate sample autocorrelations at lags 0, 1, $\ldots$, $n - 2$, though in practice only the first few lags are needed. A useful way to present the sample autocorrelations is in a bar chart with the lags on the horizontal axis. This bar chart is called the **correlogram** or **sample ACF plot**.

ACF is an abbreviation for autocorrelation function; this will be defined in Subsection 9.2.

Example 9.2   *British Government securities: the correlogram*

In Example 9.1, the time series of 1-step ahead forecast errors for monthly percentage yields on Government securities was discussed. The autocorrelation at lag 1 is 0.34, and the autocorrelation at lag 2 is 0.045. The autocorrelations at higher lags can be calculated in a similar way. However, rather than calculating and discussing each autocorrelation individually, it is more useful to show them together in a correlogram. Figure 9.3 shows the correlogram for the time series of 1-step ahead forecast errors for lags 1 to 20.

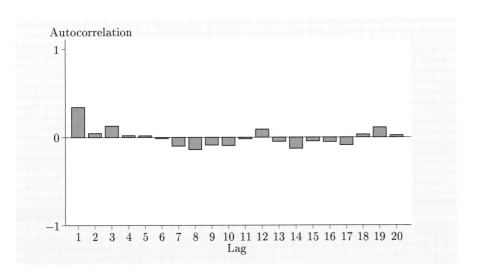

Figure 9.3   Correlogram for the forecast errors

The correlogram shown in Figure 9.3 gives an overall picture of correlations at different lags: the largest autocorrelation (in absolute value) is at lag 1, and the autocorrelations at other lags are all much closer to zero. Since the autocorrelation at lag 1 is positive, the correlogram in Figure 9.3 shows that the forecast error at time t is positively correlated with the forecast error at time $t - 1$. Thus, for example, if today's forecast is too low, it is likely that the forecast for tomorrow will be too low. As noted in Example 9.1, this suggests that it should be possible to improve on the accuracy of the forecasts produced by this forecasting method.   ◆

Correlograms are often *not* easy to interpret. However, you should look for the following two types of features.

◇   Sample autocorrelations with relatively large positive or negative values, especially for small lags, or lags that can readily be interpreted (for example, lag 4 in a quarterly series, or lag 12 in a monthly series).

◇   Patterns among the autocorrelations — for example, whether a clump of positive values is followed by a clump of negative values.

It is important not to over-interpret a correlogram, that is, to make too much of minor features. A useful rule of thumb is to identify one, or at most two, key features, if there are any.

Activity 9.2   *Average annual temperatures, 1901–2004*

In Example 7.3, Holt's exponential smoothing method was applied to the time series of annual average temperatures in Central England for 1901 to 2004. The correlogram for the forecast errors at lags 1 to 20 is shown in Figure 9.4.

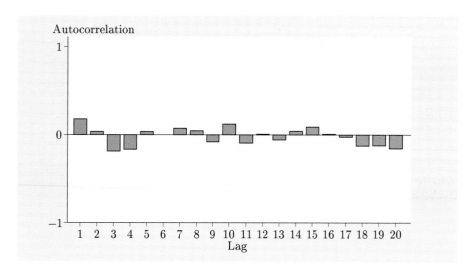

Figure 9.4   Correlogram for forecast errors for temperatures, 1901–2004

(a)   In your view, do any lags stand out as corresponding to particularly strong autocorrelations? Is there any regular pattern? In one sentence, summarize the autocorrelations between the forecast errors in this time series.

(b)   Comment briefly on what, if anything, this suggests about the possibility of improving upon these forecasts.

9.2 Tests for zero autocorrelation

The sample autocorrelations described in Subsection 9.1 are estimates of *population* autocorrelations. The (population) autocorrelation at lag k, which is denoted ρ_k, is the autocorrelation between E_{t-k} and E_t. It is assumed that ρ_k depends only on k and, in particular, that it does not depend on t. The (population) autocorrelations ρ_k, $k = 1, 2, \ldots$, define the **autocorrelation function**, or **ACF** of the time series.

The sample autocorrelation r_k is the estimated value of ρ_k, so

$$r_k = \widehat{\rho}_k.$$

The ACF is discussed in more detail in Part III.

If there is evidence of autocorrelation between the 1-step ahead forecast errors, then the forecasting method used is not the best possible: it could (in principle) be improved by using the information revealed by the autocorrelations to improve the forecasts.

Owing to random variation, even if $\rho_k = 0$ for $k \geq 1$, it is unlikely that the sample autocorrelation r_k will be exactly zero. In order to decide whether it is reasonable to conclude that $\rho_k = 0$, a significance test of the null hypothesis $\rho_k = 0$ is required.

Provided that the 1-step forecast errors have constant variance, then under the null hypothesis $\rho_k = 0$, it can be shown that the distribution of the sample autocorrelation calculated from a time series with n time points is approximately normal with mean 0 and variance $1/n$:

$$\widehat{\rho}_k \approx N\left(0, \frac{1}{n}\right).$$

The proof of the validity of this approximation is omitted.

This null distribution can be used to calculate a p value and hence test the null hypothesis $\rho_k = 0$. In practice, p values are seldom calculated. Instead, a simple graphical method is used. This is motivated as follows.

If the null hypothesis is true, the probability of obtaining a sample autocorrelation within the interval defined by the limits $\pm 1.96/\sqrt{n}$ is 0.95. Thus, if r_k lies outside the interval

$$\left(-1.96/\sqrt{n}, \ 1.96/\sqrt{n}\right),$$

then the significance probability of the test is less than 0.05 ($p < 0.05$), and hence it may be concluded that there is at least moderate evidence that the autocorrelation at lag k is different from zero.

The values $\pm 1.96/\sqrt{n}$ can be represented conveniently on the correlogram by horizontal lines. These horizontal lines are called **significance bounds**. The significance bounds greatly facilitate the interpretation of the correlogram. This is illustrated in Example 9.3.

Example 9.3 Forecasting the FTSE100 index

Holt's exponential smoothing method was used to obtain the 1-step ahead forecasts for the monthly series of logarithms of the FTSE100 index of share prices (the 'footsie' index) between January 1988 and January 2005. The autocorrelations of the forecast errors may be investigated as follows.

These data were discussed in Exercise 4.1.

The first step is to check that the forecast errors have (approximately) mean zero and constant variance. The time plot of the forecast errors is shown in Figure 9.5(a).

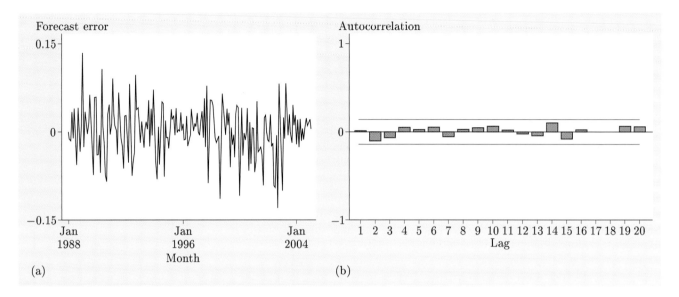

Figure 9.5 Forecast errors: (a) time plot (b) correlogram

The forecast errors appear to be centred on zero, and there is no obvious change in the level of the series. The width of the fluctuations does not vary systematically, so there is no reason to doubt the assumption of constant variance.

The correlogram for lags 1 to 20 is shown in Figure 9.5(b). The two horizontal lines on either side of the central line represent the significance bounds $\pm 1.96/\sqrt{n}$. For this series, $n = 205$, so the bounds are ± 0.137.

None of the sample autocorrelations crosses these bounds. Thus there is little evidence that any of the underlying population autocorrelations is non-zero. ♦

Activity 9.3 UK precipitation data

Simple exponential smoothing was used to obtain 1-step ahead forecasts using the UK precipitation data discussed in Example 6.3. Figure 9.6(a) shows the time plot of the forecast errors, and Figure 9.6(b) shows the correlogram for lags 1 to 20.

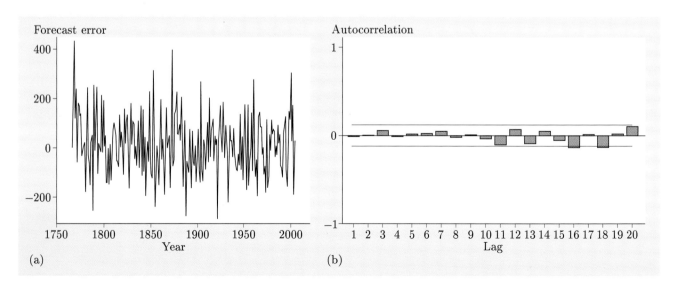

Figure 9.6 Forecast errors for UK precipitation, 1766–2004: (a) time plot (b) correlogram

(a) Does either the level or the variance of the forecast errors change
     systematically over time? (You should ignore the first few values of the time
     plot, which are affected by the choice of starting values.)

(b) For this time series, n is 239. Calculate the positions of the bounds in
     Figure 9.6(b).

(c) What does Figure 9.6(b) suggest about the presence of non-zero population
     autocorrelations at lags 1 to 20?

One problem with assessing the evidence for non-zero autocorrelations using the
significance bounds $\pm 1.96/\sqrt{n}$ is as follows. Suppose that, say, 20 sample
autocorrelations are tested in this way, and that all the underlying
autocorrelations are zero. For each k, the probability of obtaining a sample
autocorrelation lying outside the interval $(-1.96/\sqrt{n}, +1.96/\sqrt{n})$ is 5%. So, on
average, we would expect 1 out of 20 sample autocorrelations to be outside the
significance bounds by chance, even though all the underlying autocorrelations are
zero.

An alternative approach is to fix the number k of lags to be considered in
advance, and test the null hypothesis

$$H_0 : \rho_1 = \rho_2 = \cdots = \rho_k = 0.$$

Rejection of the null hypothesis means that one or more of $\rho_1, \rho_2, \ldots, \rho_k$ is
non-zero.

A test of a null hypothesis involving several autocorrelations is called a
portmanteau test. The simplest portmanteau test is based on the following test
statistic:

$$Q = n \sum_{j=1}^{k} r_j^2.$$

A *portmanteau* test combines several tests into one, just as a portmanteau *word* combines several words, as in the word *smog* (smoke and fog).

Large values of the test statistic Q provide evidence against the null hypothesis,
and lead to small p values. There are many variants of this test statistic. A
commonly used version of this portmanteau test is the **Ljung–Box test**. You
will not be required to calculate the test statistic, only to interpret significance
probabilities, so the details of the test will be omitted. You will use SPSS to carry
out the test in Section 10. The interpretation of p values in this context is
summarized in Table 9.1.

The interpretation of significance probabilities is discussed in the *Introduction to statistical modelling*. Under H_0, the Ljung–Box test statistic is approximately $\chi^2(k)$ for large n.

Table 9.1   Interpretation of p values from a portmanteau test for lags 1 to k

Significance probability p	Rough interpretation
$p > 0.10$	little evidence of autocorrelation at lags 1 to k
$0.10 \geq p > 0.05$	weak evidence of autocorrelation at lags 1 to k
$0.05 \geq p > 0.01$	moderate evidence of autocorrelation at lags 1 to k
$p \leq 0.01$	strong evidence of autocorrelation at lags 1 to k

Example 9.4   Testing for non-zero autocorrelation

Holt's exponential smoothing was used to obtain 1-step ahead forecasts for the
annual average temperature in Central England. In Activity 9.2, you found that
the autocorrelations at lags 1 to 20 between the forecast errors were all 'small'.

The value of the test statistic for the Ljung–Box test applied to these 20 sample
autocorrelations is 23.23, and the p value is 0.278. This provides little evidence of
non-zero autocorrelation at lags 1 to 20. ♦

The correlogram for forecast errors for temperatures, 1901–2004, is shown in Figure 9.4.

Activity 9.4 British Government securities

The time series of monthly yields on British Government securities was
introduced in Example 9.1. The forecast errors resulting from using Holt's
exponential smoothing to obtain 1-step ahead forecasts were discussed in
Examples 9.1 and 9.2.

(a) The value of the test statistic for the Ljung–Box test for lags 1 to 20 is 60.82,
and the p value is less than 0.0005. What do you conclude?

(b) For this time series, $n = 252$. Calculate the 95% significance bounds for
individual sample autocorrelations.

(c) The correlogram, with 95% significance bounds, is shown in Figure 9.7.

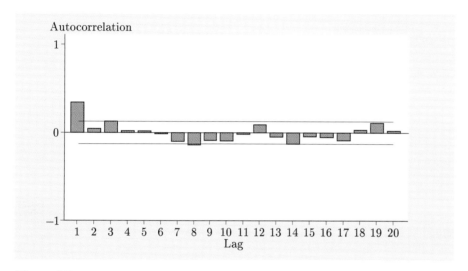

Figure 9.7 Yields on Government securities: the correlogram for forecast
errors

Identify the lags, if any, at which there is evidence that the underlying
population autocorrelations are non-zero.

In practice, it is not possible to test the hypothesis that $\rho_k = 0$ for all $k \geq 1$. Thus
both the correlogram and the Ljung–Box test require a decision to be made about
how many lags to consider. Usually, only the first few lags are of interest, together
with the lag corresponding to the seasonal period — for example, for monthly
data, the autocorrelation at lag 12 would be of particular interest. In this book,
with occasional exceptions, the first 20 lags will be considered. This choice is
made entirely on the pragmatic basis that autocorrelations at high lags are
difficult to interpret.

9.3   Prediction intervals for 1-step ahead forecasts

A 1-step ahead forecast is a point estimate: it gives a single forecasted value. As
with any estimate, some measure of the uncertainty surrounding it is required. In
the context of forecasts, such a measure of uncertainty is provided by a
prediction interval.

A **$100(1 - \alpha)\%$ prediction interval** for X_{n+1}, given observed values up to and
including x_n, is an interval with probability $1 - \alpha$ of containing X_{n+1}.

In keeping with standard
notation, the Greek letter α is
used both in connection with
prediction intervals, and to
denote the smoothing parameter
of an exponential smoothing
method. Which is referred to
should be clear from the
context.

A prediction interval is superficially similar to a confidence interval, with one important difference. A confidence interval relates to a parameter, but a prediction interval relates to a *random variable*, in this case the next value of the time series X_t. Note that it is not necessary to appeal to plausible ranges or repeated sampling of the time series to interpret a prediction interval: the definition given here is valid because X_{n+1} is a random variable, not a fixed parameter.

Example 9.5   *Forecasting temperatures*

In Example 7.3, 1-step ahead forecasts of annual average temperatures for Central England were discussed. Holt's exponential smoothing method was applied to the data for 1901 to 2004: the optimal parameter values were $\alpha = 0.05$ and $\gamma = 0.36$, with $SSE = 25.32$.

The time plot and the correlogram for the 1-step ahead forecast errors are shown in Figure 9.8.

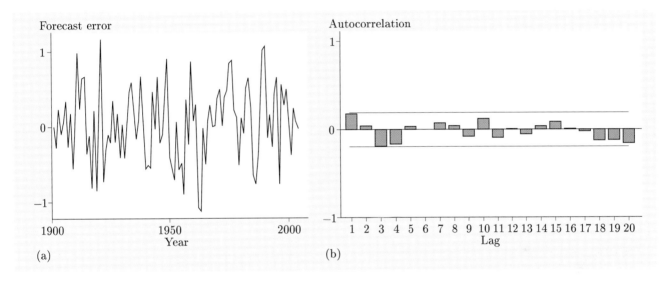

Figure 9.8   Forecast errors for annual average temperatures, 1901–2004: (a) time plot (b) correlogram

The time plot suggests that the forecast errors fluctuate around zero with constant variance. The value of the Ljung–Box test statistic for the autocorrelations up to lag 20 is 23.23, and the p value is 0.28. This provides little evidence of non-zero autocorrelations, a conclusion reinforced by the correlogram. This analysis of the forecast errors does not suggest that the forecasts could be improved upon.

Using this method with the optimal parameter values, the forecasted average temperature for 2005 is 10.59°C. How accurate is this forecast, assuming that it is valid to extrapolate to 2005? Some indication of the likely accuracy of the forecast is provided by the spread of the forecast errors in Figure 9.8(a), which lie roughly in the range −1°C to +1°C. Very large fluctuations (in relation to the range of the data) would indicate that past forecasts have been inaccurate, and hence that the forecast for the next year may also be inaccurate. On the other hand, small fluctuations might suggest that, since past forecast errors were small, the forecast for the next year is likely to be accurate. ◆

In Example 9.5, it was suggested that past forecast errors might be used as a guide to indicate how accurate the forecast for the next time period might be. Specifically, the *distribution* of past forecast errors can be used to obtain a prediction interval for X_{n+1}.

Suppose that the forecast errors E_t are normally distributed with mean zero and variance σ^2, and that the (population) autocorrelations at all lags $k \geq 1$ are zero. It follows that E_{n+1}, the 1-step ahead forecast error for X_{n+1}, is normally distributed with mean zero and variance σ^2. Thus

$$X_{n+1} - \widehat{x}_{n+1} = E_{n+1} \sim N(0, \sigma^2),$$

and hence

$$X_{n+1} \sim N\left(\widehat{x}_{n+1}, \sigma^2\right).$$

Let z denote the $(1 - \alpha/2)$-quantile of the standard normal distribution. Then X_{n+1} lies in the interval $(\widehat{x}_{n+1} - z\sigma,\ \widehat{x}_{n+1} + z\sigma)$ with probability $1 - \alpha$. To obtain a $100(1 - \alpha)\%$ prediction interval, σ is replaced by an estimate $\widehat{\sigma}$. The following estimate based on the sum of squared forecast errors will be used:

$$\widehat{\sigma} = \sqrt{\frac{SSE}{n}}.$$

Thus an approximate $100(1 - \alpha)\%$ prediction interval for X_{n+1} is $\left(x_{n+1}^-,\ x_{n+1}^+\right)$, where the **prediction limits**, x_{n+1}^- and x_{n+1}^+, are given by

$$x_{n+1}^- = \widehat{x}_{n+1} - z\sqrt{\frac{SSE}{n}}, \quad x_{n+1}^+ = \widehat{x}_{n+1} + z\sqrt{\frac{SSE}{n}}. \tag{9.1}$$

This prediction interval is approximate because σ has been estimated. The SSE, and hence $\widehat{\sigma}$, also depends on the choice of initial values, though their effect may be ignored when n is large.

Example 9.6   *Prediction interval for next year's average temperature*

In Example 7.3, Holt's exponential smoothing method was used to produce 1-step ahead forecasts for the annual average temperature in Central England using data for 1901 to 2004. The forecasted average temperature for 2005 was 10.59°C. In this example, a 95% prediction interval for the average temperature in 2005 will be obtained.

Before calculating the prediction interval, the following assumptions upon which the prediction limits depend must be checked: the forecast errors are normally distributed with mean zero and constant variance; and the autocorrelations between forecast errors are zero at lags $k \geq 1$.

Figure 9.8(a) suggests that the forecast errors fluctuate around zero, with roughly constant variance. In Example 9.5, you saw that Figure 9.8(b) and the Ljung–Box test suggest that the autocorrelations are zero — at least until lag 20, and it is not likely that temperatures in years more than 20 years apart are correlated. A histogram can be used to check that the distribution of the past forecast errors is approximately normal: a histogram of the past forecast errors is shown in Figure 9.9.

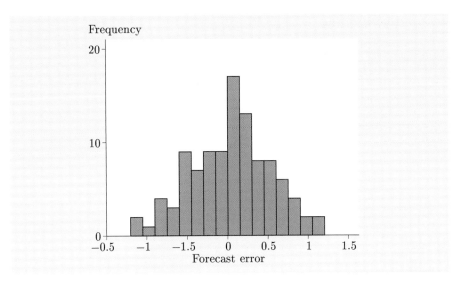

Figure 9.9   A histogram of the forecast errors

This histogram suggests that the normal assumption is reasonable. Thus all the assumptions are satisfied, so a prediction interval for X_{n+1} (corresponding to the year 2005), based on the forecast $\widehat{x}_{n+1} = 10.59$, can be calculated using (9.1).

Formal tests of normality are available, but will not be used in this book.

For a 95% prediction interval, $\alpha = 0.05$, so $1 - \alpha/2 = 0.975$ and hence the 0.975-quantile of the standard normal distribution is required: this is 1.960. The SSE is 25.32, and this is based on 104 annual temperatures from 1901 to 2004. Therefore the prediction limits, x_{n+1}^- and x_{n+1}^+, are given by

A table of quantiles of the standard normal distribution is given in the *Handbook*.

$$x_{n+1}^- = \widehat{x}_{n+1} - z\sqrt{\frac{SSE}{n}} = 10.59 - 1.96\sqrt{\frac{25.32}{104}} \simeq 9.62,$$

$$x_{n+1}^+ = \widehat{x}_{n+1} + z\sqrt{\frac{SSE}{n}} = 10.59 + 1.96\sqrt{\frac{25.32}{104}} \simeq 11.56.$$

The results may be summarized as follows. The forecasted average temperature for 2005, based on observed temperatures from 1901 to 2004, is about 10.6°C, with approximate 95% prediction interval $(9.6, 11.6)$. ♦

The method for calculating prediction intervals is summarized in the following box.

Prediction interval for a 1-step ahead forecast

Suppose that a 1-step ahead forecast $\widehat{x}_{n+1}$ for X_{n+1} has been obtained, together with SSE, the sum of squared forecast errors at times $1, 2, \ldots, n$. An approximate $100(1 - \alpha)\%$ **prediction interval** for X_{n+1} is given by

$$\left(\widehat{x}_{n+1} - z\sqrt{\frac{SSE}{n}},\ \widehat{x}_{n+1} + z\sqrt{\frac{SSE}{n}} \right),$$

where z is the $(1 - \alpha/2)$-quantile of the standard normal distribution.

The following assumptions should be checked before the prediction interval is calculated.

◇   The forecast errors are normally distributed with mean zero and constant variance σ^2.

◇   The autocorrelations between the forecast errors are zero at lags $k \geq 1$.

A time series X_t for which the X_t are normally distributed with mean zero and constant variance σ^2, and for which the autocorrelations at lags $k \geq 1$ are all zero, is called **white noise**. Thus the assumptions required to calculate a prediction interval are equivalent to requiring that the time series of forecast errors is white noise.

Activity 9.5   Predicting a chemical concentration

In Activity 4.2, a time series of the concentration level of a chemical process was discussed. The time series consists of 197 successive two-hourly readings at $2, 4, \ldots, 394$ hours. Simple exponential smoothing is used to obtain 1-step ahead forecasts. Figure 9.10 shows the time plot and a histogram of the forecast errors.

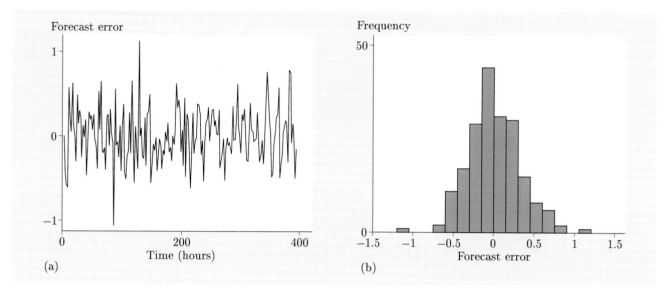

Figure 9.10   Forecast errors: (a) time plot (b) histogram

The value of the Ljung–Box test statistic for lags 1 to 20 is 29.16, and the p value is 0.085. The SSE is 19.89.

(a) Discuss the validity of the assumptions required for calculating a prediction interval for the concentration at time 396 hours.

(b) The forecasted value at time 396 hours is $\widehat{x}_{198} = 17.50$. Obtain a 95% prediction interval for X_{198}.

(c) Summarize the results.

The forecasting methods that have been discussed all depend on the assumption that the time series may be described by an additive model. When this is not the case, the methods can still be used if a transformation can be found such that the transformed time series may be represented by an additive model. The forecasting methods can then be applied to the transformed time series to obtain forecasts and prediction intervals, and these can be 'transformed back' to give forecasts and prediction intervals on the scale of the original time series. This idea is illustrated in Example 9.7.

Example 9.7   Visits abroad

In Activity 1.1, the monthly time series of numbers of (thousands of) visits abroad by UK residents for 1980 to 2004 was described. In Example 2.4, it was suggested that an additive model may be appropriate to represent the time series of square roots of the numbers of visits.

The Holt–Winters method was used to obtain a forecast for January 2005, based on data up to December 2004. The forecasted value, on the square root scale, was 62.50, with 95% prediction interval $(59.06, 65.94)$. However, a forecast and prediction interval are required on the original scale.

Values on the square root scale can be transformed to give values on the original scale by taking squares. Thus the forecasted number of thousands of visits abroad for January 2005 is $62.50^2 \simeq 3906$, and the 95% prediction limits (in thousands) are $59.06^2 \simeq 3488$ and $65.94^2 \simeq 4348$.

The interpretation of the prediction limits is as follows: the probability that the number of visits abroad in January 2005 will lie between $3\,488\,000$ and $4\,348\,000$ is 0.95.   ◆

The method illustrated in Example 9.7 will work for any monotonic transformation and, in particular, for any increasing transformation. Suppose that the time series on the original scale is Y_t and that an increasing function g is used to transform Y_t to give the time series $X_t = g(Y_t)$. If a forecast $\widehat{x}_{n+1}$ and a prediction interval (x_{n+1}^-, x_{n+1}^+) are obtained on the transformed scale, then on the original scale, the forecast is $\widehat{y}_{n+1}$, where

$$g(\widehat{y}_{n+1}) = \widehat{x}_{n+1},$$

and the prediction limits are y_{n+1}^- and y_{n+1}^+, where

$$g(y_{n+1}^-) = x_{n+1}^-, \quad g(y_{n+1}^+) = x_{n+1}^+.$$

So the forecast $\widehat{y}_{n+1}$ and the prediction limits y_{n+1}^- and y_{n+1}^+ can be obtained by applying the inverse of the function g to $\widehat{x}_{n+1}$, x_{n+1}^- and x_{n+1}^+.

This method will work with the logarithm transformation and the power transformations used in this course. For example, if the log transformation is used to transform a time series, then a forecast and prediction limits on the log scale can be transformed back to the original scale using the exponential function.

A transformation is monotonic if its graph is either increasing or decreasing.

Activity 9.6   *Predicting the FTSE100 index*

In Example 9.3, the logarithms of the FTSE100 index values between January 1988 and January 2005 were analysed using Holt's exponential smoothing.

Using this method, the predicted value for February 2005, on the log scale, is 8.490. The SSE is 0.3737, calculated using 205 observations to January 2005. You may assume that the forecast errors are white noise; that is, they are normally distributed with mean zero and constant variance, and the autocorrelations are zero at lags $k \geq 1$.

(a) Obtain an approximate 99% prediction interval for the log FTSE100 index for February 2005.

(b) Obtain a forecast and 99% prediction interval for the FTSE100 index for February 2005.

Summary of Section 9

In this section, the sample autocorrelations of the 1-step ahead forecast errors have been defined. You have learned how to use these to investigate the performance of a forecasting method. The correlogram and the Ljung–Box test for zero autocorrelation have been discussed. The calculation of approximate prediction intervals for 1-step ahead forecasts has been described. You have learned how to check the assumptions required for these calculations.

Exercises on Section 9

Exercise 9.1   Forecast errors for house prices

The Holt–Winters method was applied to the data on the logarithms of monthly average house prices between January 1996 and January 2005.

See Activity 7.1.

(a) The series comprises 109 time points. The sample autocorrelation of the 1-step ahead forecast errors at lag 12 is $r_{12} = -0.244$. Calculate the significance bounds, and hence evaluate the evidence against the null hypothesis that $\rho_{12} = 0$.

(b) The value of the Ljung–Box test statistic for autocorrelations at lags 1 to 20 is 26.55, and the p value is 0.148. What do you conclude from this?

(c) The correlogram for lags 1 to 20 is shown in Figure 9.11.

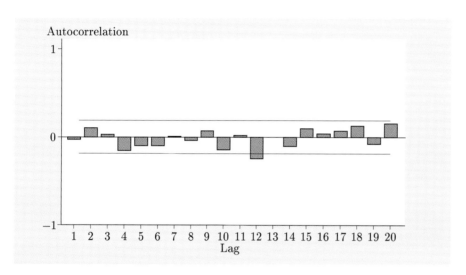

Figure 9.11   Correlogram for forecast errors for log house prices

Explain why the correlogram does not necessarily contradict the finding of part (b).

Exercise 9.2   Prediction interval for house prices

This exercise is based on the data and smoothing method described in Exercise 9.1. The time plot and a histogram of the 1-step ahead forecast errors are shown in Figure 9.12.

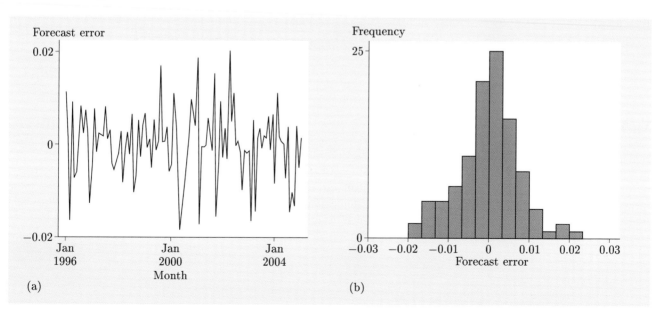

Figure 9.12   Forecast errors for the logarithms of average house prices: (a) time plot (b) histogram

The forecasted value of the logarithm of the average house price for February 2005 is 11.937. The SSE, calculated using 109 values, is 0.006 21.

(a) You may assume that the autocorrelations at lags $k \geq 1$ are zero (see Exercise 9.1). Use Figure 9.12 to check the remaining assumptions required to use (9.1) to calculate a prediction interval for the February 2005 value.

(b) Calculate an approximate 95% prediction interval for X_{110}, the logarithm of the average house price in February 2005.

(c) Obtain a forecast and 95% prediction interval for the average house price in February 2005, and summarize your results. Give your answers to the nearest £100.

10   Autocorrelation and model checking in SPSS

In this section, you will learn how to use SPSS to obtain the correlogram for the 1-step ahead forecast errors, to carry out the Ljung–Box test, and to check normality assumptions.

Refer to Chapter 6 of Computer Book 2 for the work in this section.

Summary of Section 10

In this section, you have learned how to use SPSS to obtain the correlogram for the 1-step ahead forecast errors, and to carry out the Ljung–Box test. You have also learned how to superimpose a normal curve on a histogram to check normality.

Part III ARIMA models

Introduction to Part III

In Parts I and II, moving averages were used to estimate the components of a time series X_t that can be described adequately by an additive decomposition model, and to obtain forecasts using exponential smoothing. The additive decomposition model specifies how the trend, the seasonal component and the irregular component are combined, but otherwise makes no assumptions about the correlations between successive values of X_t. Avoiding any such assumptions is both a strength and a weakness. It is a strength because the forecasting methods described will work whatever the underlying correlation structure of the time series. But it is also a weakness, since the correlation structure can help throw light on the process generating the data, and can be used to produce more accurate forecasts.

In Section 9, you learned how to obtain prediction intervals for 1-step ahead forecasts obtained by exponential smoothing. These prediction intervals require that the 1-step ahead forecast errors are uncorrelated, and normally distributed. But if they are not, then more general methods of analysis are required.

In Part III, the additive decomposition model is extended to include a statistical model for the irregular component W_t that allows explicitly for non-zero autocorrelations. A family of models known as integrated autoregressive moving average models, or ARIMA models, is discussed. These models were popularized in the 1960s by George Box and Gwilym Jenkins, and for this reason are sometimes also referred to as Box–Jenkins models.

ARIMA modelling of time series involves some advanced mathematics. All of the more difficult mathematics will be sidestepped so as to concentrate on the practical aspects of the models. To keep matters simple, only non-seasonal time series will be considered. In Section 11, an important family of time series, the stationary series, is introduced. In Section 12, a class of models known as autoregressive models is discussed. In Section 13, a further class of models, the moving average models, is described. In Section 14, autoregressive models and moving average models are brought together as ARIMA models. Finally, in Section 15, you will learn how to use SPSS to analyse time series using ARIMA models.

ARIMA models can be extended to cope with seasonality, but these extensions will be omitted.

11 Stationary time series

In this section, the family of stationary time series is introduced. The models described in subsequent sections apply to stationary time series. Thus, if a time series is not stationary, the first step in choosing a model for it will be to transform it into a stationary series.

In Subsection 11.1, stationary time series are defined and illustrated. Then, in Subsection 11.2, methods for transforming time series into stationary time series are discussed. One method of particular importance is called differencing. In Subsection 11.3, you will learn how to use SPSS to obtain stationary series.

11.1 Stationarity

In general terms, a time series is said to be stationary if its basic statistical properties do not vary over time. Stationarity is an important idea in time series analysis. It is important because it provides a basis for forecasting: if the statistical properties of the time series do not change, then there is some chance of obtaining good forecasts by extrapolation (though this is never guaranteed).

The most basic of statistical properties are the mean and variance. A time series X_t is said to be **stationary in mean** if it has constant mean:

$$E(X_t) = \mu.$$

In particular, this implies that there is no increasing or decreasing trend, and no seasonality (or any other cyclic variation).

A time series is said to be **stationary in variance** if it has constant variance:

$$V(X_t) = \sigma^2.$$

This means that the size of the irregular fluctuations must be roughly the same at every time point. Note that a time series that is stationary both in mean and in variance can be written in the additive form

$$X_t = \mu + W_t,$$

where the irregular component W_t has mean zero and variance σ^2.

Example 11.1   Stationarity in mean and in variance

The time plots of four time series are shown in Figure 11.1.

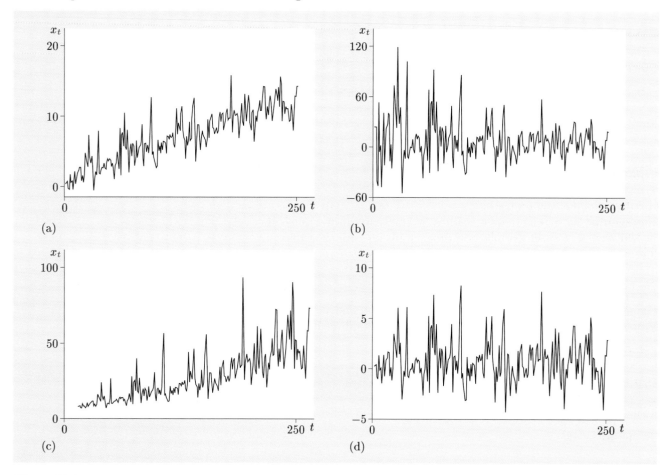

Figure 11.1   Four time series

The time series in Figure 11.1(a) displays a trend, though the variance of the irregular component appears constant: this time series is stationary in variance, but it is not stationary in mean. Figure 11.1(b) shows a time series with no trend, but decreasing variance: this time series is stationary in mean but it is not stationary in variance. Figure 11.1(c) shows a time series with increasing trend and variance: this time series is stationary neither in mean nor in variance. In fact, it can be described by a multiplicative model. Figure 11.1(d) shows a time series with no trend and constant variance: this time series is stationary in both mean and variance.   ◆

Deciding whether a time series is stationary in mean and in variance is done most easily by examining a time plot. In fact, you have already done this: in Subsection 1.2, you examined time plots to identify trends, and in Subsection 9.3, to check that the variance of the 1-step ahead forecast errors is constant.

A further type of stationarity is important in time series analysis. This is the requirement that the autocorrelation between X_t and X_{t-k} does not vary with t, but depends only on the lag k. This characteristic is called **stationarity in correlation**. Stationarity in correlation is required to define the autocorrelation function ρ_k, which is the underlying autocorrelation between X_t and X_{t-k}.

In Subsection 9.2, it was assumed that the autocorrelation between the 1-step ahead forecast errors at times t and $t - k$ depended only on the lag k. In other words, it was assumed that the forecast errors were stationary in correlation.

Stationarity in correlation cannot usually be checked by inspecting a time plot. For this reason, it is usually *assumed* that a time series is stationary in correlation, unless there is good reason to believe it is not — for instance, because of a change in the process generating the data.

A time series is said to be **stationary** if it is stationary in mean, in variance and in correlation. This definition is set out in the following box.

There are other definitions of stationarity. The one given here is sometimes called *weak* stationarity.

Stationarity

A time series X_t is **stationary** if it satisfies the following conditions.

◇ $E(X_t) = \mu$ (constant mean).

◇ $V(X_t) = \sigma^2$ (constant variance).

◇   For all k, ρ_k, the autocorrelation between X_t and X_{t-k}, depends only on the lag k.

Example 11.2   White noise

In Subsection 9.3, the term white noise was defined: a time series X_t is said to be *white noise* if $X_t \sim N(0, \sigma^2)$ and successive terms are uncorrelated. It follows that for white noise, the autocorrelations ρ_k are such that $\rho_k = 0$ for $k \geq 1$. White noise is therefore a stationary time series.   ◆

Non-stationarity induces patterns in the autocorrelations that make them even more difficult interpret. This is illustrated in Example 11.3.

Example 11.3   Non-stationarity and autocorrelations

Figure 11.1(a) was obtained by adding a trend component to the time series shown in Figure 11.1(d). Figure 11.2 shows the effect of this trend on the correlogram.

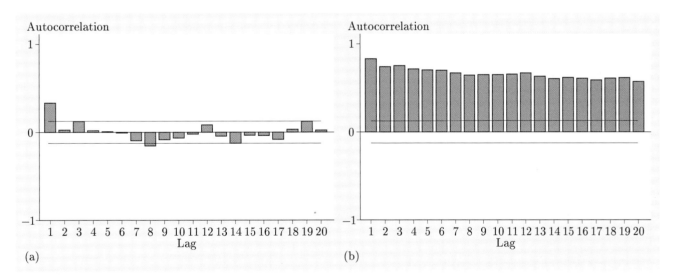

Figure 11.2   Correlograms for two time series

Figure 11.2(a) shows the correlogram for the time series in Figure 11.1(d). There is a relatively large positive sample autocorrelation at lag 1 — it exceeds the upper significance bound — but the other sample autocorrelations lie within or only just cross the significance bounds: it is reasonable to conclude that autocorrelations at lags greater than 1 are zero. Figure 11.2(b) shows the correlogram for the time series in Figure 11.1(a).

Adding a trend to the time series changes the sample ACF completely: now all sample autocorrelations up to lag 20 (and well beyond) are large and positive, and exceed the significance bounds. The autocorrelations are large and positive because, owing to the trend, a small value x_t tends to be preceded by small values at times before t, while a large value x_t tends to be followed by large values at times after t.   ◆

Recall that ACF is an abbreviation for autocorrelation function.

85

It is generally impossible to interpret the correlogram for a non-stationary time series in any useful way. For this reason, correlograms should be used primarily to investigate stationary time series. Activity 11.1 provides another example of the effect of non-stationarity on the correlogram.

Activity 11.1 *Correlograms and seasonality*

The time plots of two monthly time series are shown in Figures 11.3(a) and 11.3(b). The correlograms corresponding to the time series in Figures 11.3(a) and 11.3(b) are shown in Figures 11.3(c) and 11.3(d), respectively.

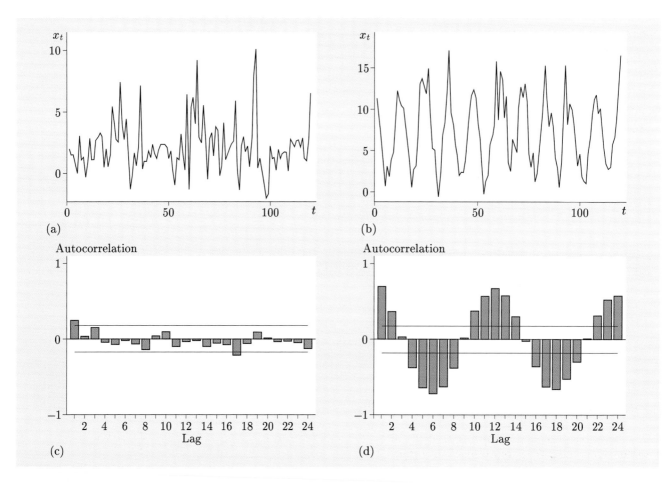

Figure 11.3   Two time plots and corresponding correlograms

(a)   Use the time plots in Figures 11.3(a) and 11.3(b) to decide whether each of the time series is stationary or non-stationary. Explain your decision in each case.

(b)   The time series in Figure 11.3(b) was obtained from that in Figure 11.3(a) by adding a component to it. In general terms, what sort of component do you think was added?

(c)   Describe the main difference between the two correlograms. Explain in general terms why the transformation you identified in part (b) has produced the large positive sample autocorrelations at lags 12 and 24, and the large negative sample autocorrelations at lags 6 and 18, shown in Figure 11.3(d).

11.2   Differencing time series

Suppose that a non-seasonal time series X_t can be described using an additive model of the form

$$X_t = m_t + W_t,$$

where m_t is the trend component and W_t is the irregular component with mean zero and constant variance. A standard method of analysis is to estimate the trend component as described in Part I, then subtract the estimated trend from the series, and thus obtain an estimate of the irregular component. Provided that the trend has been fully removed, the estimated irregular component can be assumed to be stationary, and hence its correlation structure can be investigated using a correlogram.

A second approach is to remove the trend without estimating it explicitly. This is achieved by **differencing** the series, as follows. Suppose first that the trend component is linear, so that for some constants m and b,

$$m_t = m + b \times t.$$

The idea behind differencing is to replace X_t by Y_t, the difference between X_t and X_{t-1}:

$$
\begin{aligned}
Y_t &= X_t - X_{t-1} \\
&= (m + bt + W_t) - (m + b(t-1) + W_{t-1}) \\
&= (m + bt + W_t) - (m + bt + W_{t-1} - b) \\
&= b + W_t - W_{t-1} \\
&= b + W_t',
\end{aligned}
$$

where $W_t' = W_t - W_{t-1}$. Note that the time series Y_t has constant level (since b is a constant) and irregular component W_t'. The new time series Y_t is called the **series of first differences** of X_t, or alternatively the time series of **differences of order 1**.

The time series of first differences is obtained because, although the original time series X_t is not stationary in mean, the series of first differences is stationary in mean.

Throughout the rest of Part III, only non-seasonal time series are considered.

Example 11.4   First differences

The time series of monthly percentage yields on British Government securities between 1950 and 1970 is reproduced in Figure 11.4(a).

See Example 9.1.

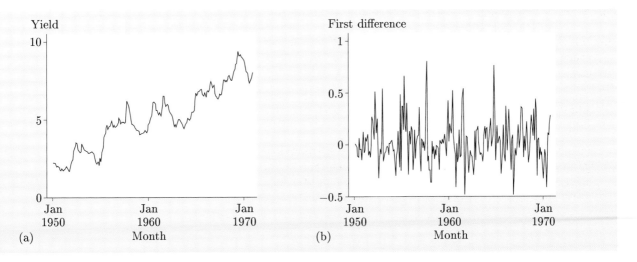

Figure 11.4   Monthly yields: (a) original data (b) first differences

87

The original time series is known to be non-seasonal, but it has a clear rising linear trend. Table 11.1 shows the first few values of the time series and the corresponding first differences

Table 11.1   Monthly yields and first differences, January 1950–June 1950

Month	Yield	First differences
January	2.22	–
February	2.23	0.01
March	2.22	−0.01
April	2.20	−0.02
May	2.09	−0.11
June	1.97	−0.12

The first difference for January 1950 cannot be calculated from these data, since the value for December 1949 is not available. So the corresponding cell is left blank in Table 11.1. The first difference for February 1950 is

$$y_2 = x_2 - x_1$$
$$= 2.23 - 2.22$$
$$= 0.01.$$

The other first differences are calculated similarly. The time series of first differences is shown in Figure 11.4(b). The increasing trend has been removed, and the resulting time series can be assumed to be stationary. ♦

In fact, this series of first differences was used as the basis for Figures 11.1 and 11.3.

So far it has been assumed that the original series X_t has a linear trend. But what happens if the trend is curved? In that case, the series of first differences might not be stationary in mean, but it will be 'less curved' than the original series. So the procedure is repeated. A third series, Z_t, is obtained by taking the first differences of the Y_t:

$$Z_t = Y_t - Y_{t-1}$$
$$= (X_t - X_{t-1}) - (X_{t-1} - X_{t-2})$$
$$= X_t - 2X_{t-1} + X_{t-2}.$$

This time series is called the **series of second differences** of X_t, or the time series of **differences of order 2**. (Note that the series of second differences is *not* the same as the series $X_t - X_{t-2}$.) If the original time series X_t has a quadratic trend component,

$$m_t = m + bt + at^2,$$

then it can be shown that the series of second differences will be stationary in mean. The key point is that you can keep taking differences in this way until you obtain a series that is stationary in mean, and that you can do so without estimating the trend component of the original time series.

Example 11.5   The UK index of production

The time plot of the (seasonally adjusted) quarterly UK index of production, between the first quarter of 1990 and the first quarter of 2005, is shown in Figure 11.5.

These data were obtained in June 2005 from the National Statistics website www.statistics.gov.uk.

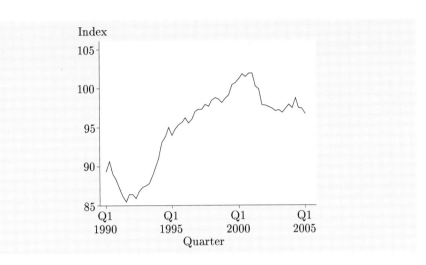

Figure 11.5   UK index of production

The series is non-seasonal, since the seasonal component has been removed by seasonal adjustment. The irregular fluctuations do not vary in size, so the series may be described using an additive model. However, the series is not stationary, as there is clear variation in the level of the series over time. An initial drop (between 1990 and 1992) is followed by a rise until about 2001, then followed by another drop. The trend is certainly not linear.

The time plot of the series of first differences is shown in Figure 11.6(a).

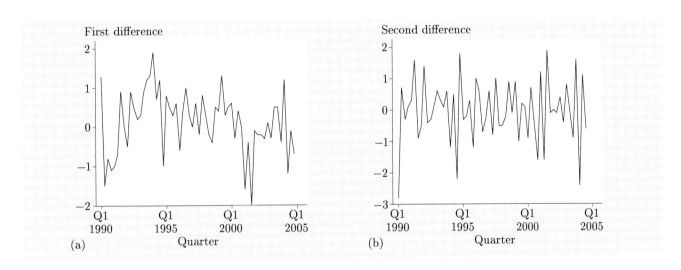

Figure 11.6   Index of production: (a) first differences (b) second differences

This time plot suggests that the series of first differences may not be stationary in mean: after the first value, there is an increasing trend until 1993, followed by a more gradual decline. However, the variation in the level is much less marked than for the original data. Thus the first differences have reduced, but not completely removed, the trend.

The time plot of the series of second differences is shown in Figure 11.6(b). This time series is clearly stationary in mean. There is no systematic increase or decrease in the variance, so the series also appears to be stationary in variance. ◆

Activity 11.2   *Obtaining a differenced time series*

Table 11.2 contains the first six values of the time series of the UK index of production discussed in Example 11.5.

Obtain the first and the second differences corresponding to these values.

Table 11.2   Index of production

Period	Index
Quarter 1, 1990	89.3
Quarter 2, 1990	90.6
Quarter 3, 1990	89.1
Quarter 4, 1990	88.3
Quarter 1, 1991	87.2
Quarter 2, 1991	86.2

In Example 11.5, you saw that stationarity in mean can be obtained by repeated differencing of the time series. However, note that you should not difference a time series more times than is necessary to obtain approximate stationarity. Once approximate stationarity has been achieved, further differencing is unnecessary and may make it more difficult to model the time series. Differencing too much is called **over-differencing**, and should be avoided. It is seldom necessary to use differencing of order greater than 2.

Activity 11.3   *Differencing the Central England temperatures*

The time plot of the annual average Central England temperatures for 1901 to 2004 is shown in Figure 11.7.

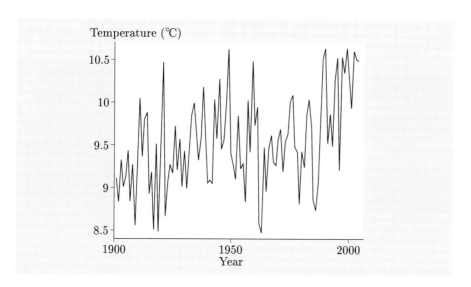

Figure 11.7   Annual average temperatures in Central England, 1901–2004

The time plots of the first differences and the second differences are shown in Figures 11.8(a) and 11.8(b), respectively.

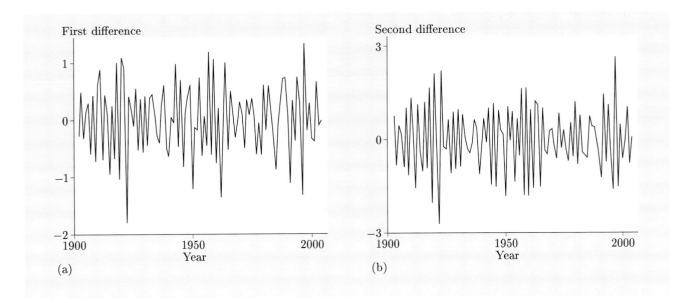

Figure 11.8   Central England temperatures: (a) first differences (b) second differences

(a) Briefly describe the time series in Figure 11.7, and the effects of taking first differences and second differences.

(b) Which order of differencing is appropriate to achieve approximate stationarity in mean for the time series of Central England temperatures?

(c) Explain why the time plot corresponding to your answer to part (b) suggests that the differenced series is stationary.

11.3   Differencing in SPSS

In this subsection, you will learn how to use SPSS to produce time plots of first differences and differences of higher order so as to determine the order of differencing required to produce a time series that is stationary in mean. You will also learn how to transform a time series using logarithms and obtain time plots of differences of the transformed time series.

Refer to Chapter 7 of Computer Book 2 for the work in this subsection.

Summary of Section 11

In this section, stationarity of a time series has been defined. You have learned how to recognize non-stationarity in mean and in variance from a time plot. The method of differencing has been introduced. You have learned how to use SPSS to difference a time series and, if necessary, transform it using logarithms in order to obtain approximate stationarity.

Exercises on Section 11

Exercise 11.1   Stationarity in mean and variance

The time plot of a non-seasonal time series is shown in Figure 11.9.

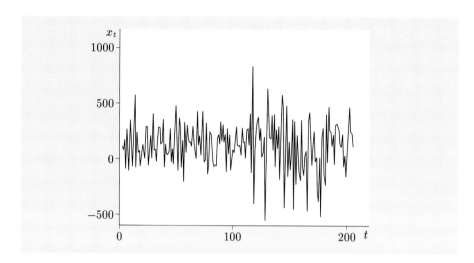

Figure 11.9   A non-seasonal time series

Is the time series stationary in mean? Is it stationary in variance? Explain your answers.

Exercise 11.2   Differencing a series

The time series in Figure 11.9 was obtained by differencing. Table 11.3 contains the first six values of the original (undifferenced) time series.

Obtain the second differences corresponding to these values.

Table 11.3   The original time series

Time	Value
1	1790.8
2	1768.8
3	1742.5
4	1802.2
5	1784.4
6	1857.6

12 Autoregressive models

In this section, an important family of models for stationary time series, the autoregressive models, is introduced. Autoregressive models are classified by their order. In Subsection 12.1, the autoregressive model of order 1 is defined. The definition is extended to autoregressive models of arbitrary order p in Subsection 12.2. In Subsection 12.3, a function called the partial autocorrelation function is introduced. In Subsection 12.4, identifying the order of an autoregressive model is discussed.

In this section, all time series are assumed to be stationary.

12.1 The autoregressive model of order 1

Let X_t be a stationary time series, with zero mean. The simplest model describing the correlation between successive terms of X_t is the white noise model, for which the autocorrelations are zero at all lags $k \geq 1$. However, the white noise model is very restrictive. For example, it cannot describe processes for which the past history of the process influences its future course. This is illustrated in Example 12.1.

White noise was discussed in Example 11.2.

Example 12.1 Daily sales of a dairy product

Figure 12.1 shows the time plot of daily sales of a dairy product over a 100-day period.

DeLurgio, S.A. (1998) *Forecasting Principles and Applications*. McGraw-Hill, Singapore.

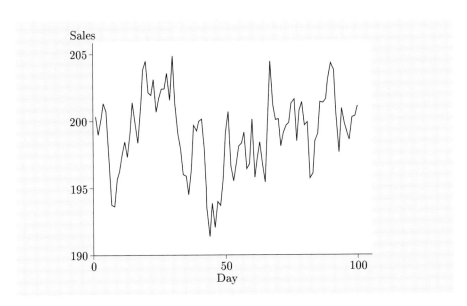

Figure 12.1 Daily sales of a dairy product

There is no clear trend in the time plot: the values appear to fluctuate around a mean of about 199. The size of the fluctuations also appears to be roughly constant over the time period. Thus there is no reason to suggest that the time series is not stationary.

To investigate possible correlations between sales at different time intervals, the correlogram is used. The correlogram is shown in Figure 12.2, together with 95% significance bounds.

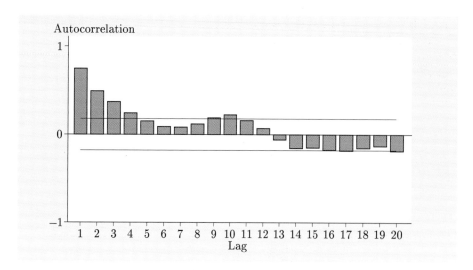

Figure 12.2   Correlogram for daily sales of a dairy product

The sample autocorrelations at lags 1, 2 and 3 clearly exceed the 95% significance bounds. Thus the correlogram indicates that the white noise model is inappropriate for this time series: sales on adjacent days are correlated.   ♦

In many situations it is appropriate to allow for the possibility that X_t might depend on previous values. A simple model allowing for this is

$$X_t = \beta X_{t-1} + Z_t,$$

The symbol β is the Greek lower-case letter beta.

where β is a constant and Z_t is white noise with mean zero and variance σ^2. Note that if $\beta = 0$, then X_t is white noise. But if $\beta \neq 0$, then there is a non-zero correlation between X_t and X_{t-1}. In order to ensure that X_t is stationary, it is necessary to impose the condition $-1 < \beta < 1$: if this condition were not satisfied, then the values of X_t would tend to increase in magnitude.

This model is the **autoregressive model of order 1**, also called the **AR(1)** model. The model may be extended to include time series X_t with mean $\mu \neq 0$, as in the following box.

Autoregressive model of order 1

Let X_t be a stationary time series with mean μ. The **autoregressive model of order 1**, or **AR(1)** model, has the following form:

$$X_t - \mu = \beta(X_{t-1} - \mu) + Z_t,$$

where β is a parameter to be estimated, $-1 < \beta < 1$, and Z_t is white noise with mean 0 and variance σ^2.

The word 'regressive' is derived from 'regression', which describes any relationship between random variables of the form $Y = \beta X + Z$, and 'auto' indicates that the X and the Y are successive terms of the same time series. The above model is of order 1 because X_t depends directly only on its immediate predecessor, X_{t-1}.

How can we decide whether the AR(1) model is appropriate for a particular time series (such as the daily sales of a dairy product discussed in Example 12.1)? One approach is to compare the sample autocorrelation function (or ACF) for the time series with the theoretical autocorrelation function for the model. If the two are similar, the model might be appropriate. If they are very different, then the model is probably not appropriate.

The ACF was introduced in Subsection 9.2.

The autocorrelation function for the AR(1) model is given by

$$\rho_k = \beta^k, \quad k = 0, 1, 2, \ldots . \tag{12.1}$$

Note that this is the *theoretical* autocorrelation function corresponding to the AR(1) model, as distinct from the sample autocorrelation function displayed in a correlogram. Since $-1 < \beta < 1$, the magnitude of ρ_k gradually tails off from $\rho_0 = 1$ as the lag k increases. If $\beta > 0$, then all the autocorrelations are positive (but eventually become very close to zero). If $\beta < 0$, then the signs of the autocorrelations alternate, positive for even lags and negative for odd lags. Figure 12.3 shows the autocorrelation functions at lags 1 to 10 for four AR(1) models with different values of β.

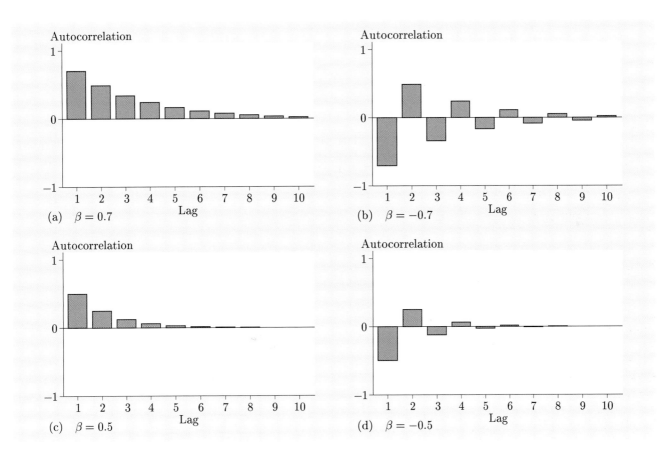

Figure 12.3   The ACFs for four AR(1) models

Note that the autocorrelations decline in magnitude more rapidly when $\beta = 0.5$ than when $\beta = 0.7$. The decline in both cases is said to be **exponential**.

Example 12.2   Daily sales of a dairy product, continued

Look again at the correlogram for the daily sales of a dairy product in Figure 12.2. There is clear evidence of positive autocorrelation up to lag 3 or 4. Thereafter, the autocorrelations lie close to or within the 95% significance bounds and should not be over-interpreted, though they display a striking pattern. If an AR(1) model were appropriate for these data, the parameter β would be positive, since otherwise the autocorrelations would alternate in sign. Using Figure 12.3 as a very rough guide, a value of β in excess of 0.5 might be appropriate, since the decline in the autocorrelations as the lag increases is not quite as rapid as when $\beta = 0.5$.

On the basis of these observations, an AR(1) model appears to be a possible model for these data. Other possibilities must be considered, and other checks must be undertaken before it can be concluded that the AR(1) model is appropriate. However, this example provides a flavour of the methods used to select an appropriate model. ◆

Activity 12.1   Chemical process data

Figure 12.4 shows the time plot of 70 successive readings from a batch chemical process, and the correlogram (with 95% significance bounds).

O'Donovan, T.M. (1983) *Short Term Forecasting: An Introduction to the Box–Jenkins Approach.* John Wiley & Sons, Chichester.

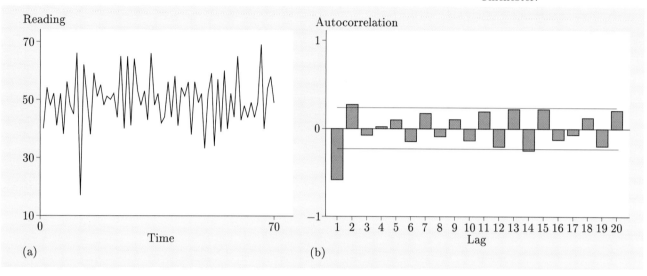

Figure 12.4   Chemical process readings: (a) time plot (b) correlogram

(a)   Is this time series stationary? Explain your answer. (You may assume that the series is non-seasonal.)

(b)   Describe the main features of the sample autocorrelation function.

(c)   If an AR(1) model were appropriate for these data, would the coefficient β be positive or negative?

12.2   The autoregressive model of order p

In the autoregressive model of order 1, X_t depends linearly on X_{t-1}, but is not directly related to earlier terms of the time series. In many practical settings, it is natural to assume that X_t might be directly related not only to X_{t-1}, but also to X_{t-2} and perhaps earlier terms X_{t-3}, X_{t-4}, and so on.

Suppose that X_t is a stationary time series with mean zero. A simple model that allows for the possibility that X_t is directly related to both X_{t-1} and X_{t-2} is

$$X_t = \beta_1 X_{t-1} + \beta_2 X_{t-2} + Z_t,$$

where β_1 and β_2 are constants, and Z_t is white noise with mean 0 and variance σ^2. This is the **autoregressive model of order 2**, also written **AR(2)**. If X_t has mean $\mu \neq 0$, then the AR(2) model is

$$X_t - \mu = \beta_1(X_{t-1} - \mu) + \beta_2(X_{t-2} - \mu) + Z_t.$$

In order to ensure that X_t is stationary, conditions must be imposed on the constants β_1 and β_2: if both constants are too large in magnitude, then successive terms X_t will grow in magnitude, so X_t will not be stationary. The conditions required are more complicated than for the AR(1) model and will not be given here.

Example 12.3   Viscosity data

One hundred successive measurements were made of the viscosity of a chemical product. Figure 12.5 shows the time plot and correlogram for this time series.

O'Donovan, T.M. (1983) *Short Term Forecasting: An Introduction to the Box–Jenkins Approach*. John Wiley & Sons, Chichester.

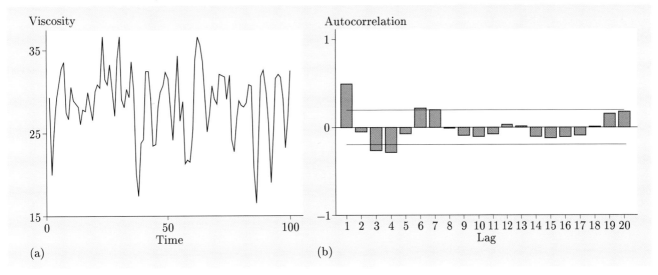

Figure 12.5   Viscosity time series: (a) time plot (b) correlogram

The time plot in Figure 12.5(a) suggests that the time series is stationary both in mean and in variance (or at least there is no compelling reason not to assume this). The correlogram shows an alternating pattern. The pattern is reminiscent of the sample ACF for an AR(1) time series with negative coefficient, with some important differences. For example, the large positive autocorrelation at lag 1 is followed not by one negative autocorrelation, but by several. These are followed by two positive autocorrelations at lags 6 and 7. The autocorrelations then dip below the 95% significance bounds.

For reasons that will be explained in Subsection 12.4, an appropriate model for this time series is the AR(2) model.   ♦

The theoretical autocorrelation function for an AR(2) model is more complicated than that for an AR(1) model. However, for all autoregressive models, the autocorrelation function either declines exponentially, or alternates in positive and negative clumps that tail off in height as the lag increases (this pattern is called **damped sinusoidal**).

The autoregressive model can be extended to include direct dependence between X_t and $X_{t-1}, X_{t-2}, \ldots, X_{t-p}$ for some arbitrary integer $p \geq 1$. The definition is given in the following box.

Autoregressive model of order p

Let X_t be a stationary time series with mean μ. The **autoregressive model of order p**, or **AR(p) model**, has the following form:

$$X_t - \mu = \beta_1(X_{t-1} - \mu) + \beta_2(X_{t-2} - \mu) + \cdots + \beta_p(X_{t-p} - \mu) + Z_t,$$

where $\beta_1, \beta_2, \ldots, \beta_p$ are parameters to be estimated, and Z_t is white noise with mean 0 and variance σ^2.

Activity 12.2   The order of an autoregressive model

In each of the models below, X_t is a stationary time series with mean zero, and Z_t is white noise. Say whether each model is an autoregressive model, giving a reason for your answer in each case. If it is an autoregressive model, state its order and write down the values of the parameters $\beta_1, \ldots, \beta_p$.

(a) $X_t = 0.5X_1 + 0.3X_2 + Z_t$

(b) $X_t = 0.6X_{t-1} - 0.2X_{t-2} - 0.05X_{t-3} + Z_t$

(c) $X_t = 0.5X_{t-1}^2 + 0.3X_{t-2} + Z_t$

(d) $X_t = -0.6X_{t-1} + 0.1X_{t-2} + Z_t$

12.3   The partial autocorrelation function

In practice, it is not usually possible to identify the order of an autoregressive model just by examining its autocorrelation function. This is illustrated in Example 12.4.

Example 12.4   Autocorrelation functions for autoregressive models

Figure 12.6 shows the theoretical autocorrelation functions at lags 1 to 15 for four autoregressive time series models.

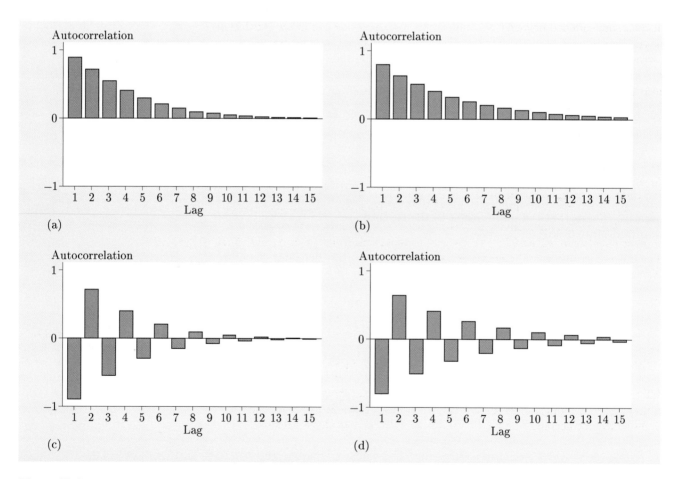

Figure 12.6   The ACFs for four autoregressive models

Figure 12.6(a) shows the ACF for the AR(2) model
$X_t = 1.2X_{t-1} - 0.35X_{t-2} + Z_t$, and is very similar to Figure 12.6(b), which shows
the ACF for the AR(1) model $X_t = 0.8X_{t-1} + Z_t$.

Similarly, Figure 12.6(c) shows the ACF for the AR(2) model
$X_t = -1.2X_{t-1} - 0.35X_{t-2} + Z_t$, which looks much the same as Figure 12.6(d),
which is the ACF for the AR(1) model $X_t = -0.8X_{t-1} + Z_t$.

For each pair of series, there are subtle differences in the values of the
autocorrelations. But it is not easy to tell which is which by inspecting these
plots. Furthermore, these are plots of the *theoretical* ACF: plots based on data
(correlograms) are less regular and harder to interpret. ♦

Example 12.4 shows that the ACF may not be of much help in identifying the
order of an autoregressive time series. However, a function called the *partial
autocorrelation function*, or PACF, can make the identification easier.

The idea behind the PACF will be explained in the context of autoregressive
models. However, note that the PACF is defined for all stationary time series, not
just for autoregressive models.

Consider the AR(1) model

$$X_t = \beta X_{t-1} + Z_t.$$

The same model, applied at time $t - 1$, gives

$$X_{t-1} = \beta X_{t-2} + Z_{t-1}.$$

The model thus specifies a direct dependence between X_t and its predecessor
X_{t-1}, and a direct dependence between X_{t-1} and X_{t-2}. These successive direct
dependencies induce an *indirect* dependence between X_t and X_{t-2}, which is
manifested as a non-zero autocorrelation β^2 at lag 2. The key point, however, is
that the dependence between X_t and X_{t-2} is *indirect*, and works through X_{t-1}:
all the dependence between X_t and X_{t-2} is accounted for by the correlation
between X_t and X_{t-1} and the correlation between X_{t-1} and X_{t-2}. There is no
direct dependence between X_t and X_{t-2}. The partial autocorrelation between X_t
and X_{t-2} is a measure of the direct dependence between X_t and X_{t-2}, so for the
AR(1) model it is zero.

The idea of direct and indirect dependence between the terms in a time series can
be used to define the partial autocorrelation between any two terms in any time
series. In general, for any time series X_t, the **partial autocorrelation** between
X_t and X_{t-k} is a measure of the dependence between X_t and X_{t-k} that is *not*
accounted for by correlations with the intermediate values
$X_{t-1}, X_{t-2}, \ldots, X_{t-k+1}$. Thus it is a measure of the *direct* dependence between
X_t and X_{t-k}. Like an ordinary autocorrelation, a partial autocorrelation is a
number α between -1 and 1. The partial autocorrelation between X_t and X_{t-k} is
zero if there is no direct dependence between them.

For a stationary time series X_t, the partial autocorrelations depend only on the
lags. The **partial autocorrelation function** or **PACF** is defined as follows:

$$\alpha_k = \text{partial autocorrelation between } X_t \text{ and } X_{t-k}, \quad k = 0, 1, \ldots .$$

The expression for α_k has been
omitted. However, you will be
expected to interpret partial
autocorrelations.

Since X_t is perfectly and directly correlated with itself, $\alpha_0 = 1$. Also, since there
are no intermediate terms between X_t and X_{t-1}, the correlation between them
must be direct, so $\alpha_1 = \rho_1$. However, for lags greater than 1, α_k and ρ_k usually
differ. The interpretation of α_k is similar to that of ρ_k: the key point to remember
is that α_k relates only to the extent of *direct* dependence at lag k, that is, to
dependence not accounted for by correlations with intermediate values.

The autoregressive model of order p for a time series X_t with zero mean is

$$X_t = \beta_1 X_{t-1} + \beta_2 X_{t-2} + \cdots + \beta_p X_{t-p} + Z_t.$$

This specifies direct dependencies between X_t and each of $X_{t-1}, X_{t-2}, \ldots, X_{t-p}$. There is no *direct* dependence between terms separated by lags greater than p, though indirect dependence between them will generally be induced by the intermediate terms. The lack of any direct dependence at lags greater than p means that the partial autocorrelations at lags greater than p are all zero. In fact, it can be shown that for an $\mathrm{AR}(p)$ model,

$$\alpha_p = \beta_p \quad \text{and} \quad \alpha_k = 0 \text{ for } k > p.$$

The fact that the PACF for an $\mathrm{AR}(p)$ model is zero at all lags greater than p, and is non-zero at lag p, can be used to identify the order of an autoregressive model. This is illustrated in Example 12.5.

Example 12.5   The PACF for an autoregressive model

The ACFs for four autoregressive models were shown in Figure 12.6. Figure 12.7 shows the theoretical partial autocorrelation functions, or PACFs, for these models.

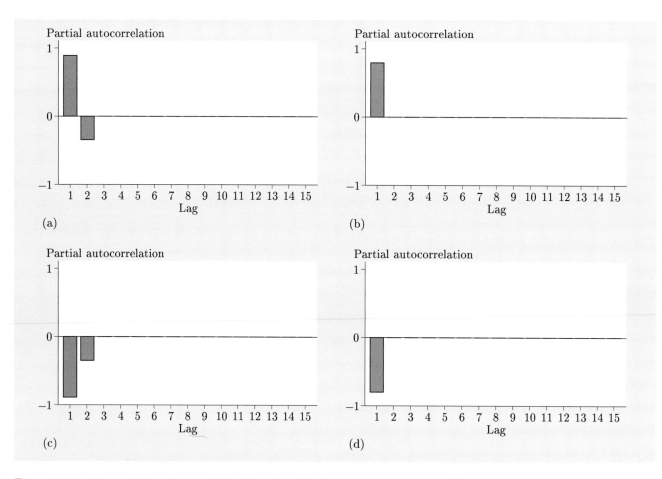

Figure 12.7   The partial autocorrelation functions for four autoregressive models

The PACFs in Figures 12.7(a) and 12.7(c) are zero after lag 2: it can therefore be concluded that these autoregressive models are of order 2. In contrast, the PACFs in Figures 12.7(b) and 12.7(d) are zero after lag 1: these autoregressive models are therefore of order 1.   ◆

Activity 12.3 *Interpreting the PACF*

Figure 12.8 shows the PACFs for two AR(p) models.

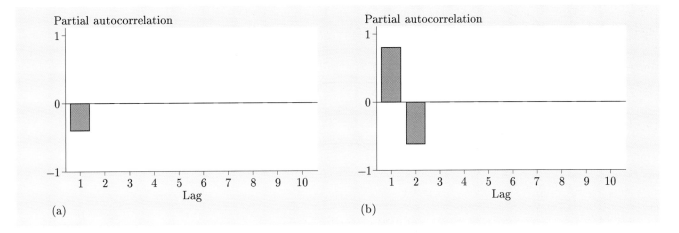

Figure 12.8 The PACFs for two AR(p) models

In each case, identify the value of p, and obtain a rough estimate of β_p.

12.4 *Identifying the order of an autoregressive model*

The partial autocorrelations can be estimated from a time series $x_1, x_2, \ldots, x_n$, giving rise to the **sample PACF**: for each k, the sample partial autocorrelation $\widehat{\alpha}_k$ is an estimate of the partial autocorrelation α_k. Details of how the PACF is estimated are omitted: calculation of the sample PACF is done by computer.

The interpretation of the sample PACF is similar to that of the sample ACF, which was described in Subsection 9.1.

If the underlying model were the white noise model, then all the partial autocorrelations would be zero. Under the null hypothesis of zero partial autocorrelation, the distributions of the sample partial autocorrelations for a time series with n observations are approximately $N(0, 1/n)$. Thus a sample partial autocorrelation $\widehat{\alpha}_k$ greater than $+1.96/\sqrt{n}$ or less than $-1.96/\sqrt{n}$ may be interpreted as providing at least moderate evidence against the null hypothesis $\alpha_k = 0$.

The sample ACF is represented as a bar chart (the correlogram), and the sample PACF is also represented as a bar chart. The bar chart for the sample PACF is called the **partial correlogram**, or **sample PACF plot**. Only sample partial autocorrelations at lags 1 to 20 will usually be shown. Significance bounds are often drawn as horizontal lines at $-1.96/\sqrt{n}$ and $+1.96/\sqrt{n}$ on the partial correlogram. These provide a guide for deciding which of the underlying partial autocorrelations are non-zero.

Example 12.6   Sample PACF for the viscosity data

In Example 12.3, a stationary time series of viscosity measurements was discussed. The partial correlogram for this time series for lags 1 to 20 is shown in Figure 12.9.

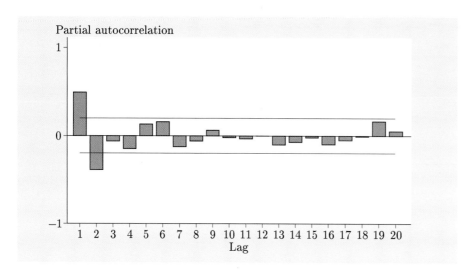

Figure 12.9   Partial correlogram for the viscosity data

The sample partial autocorrelations at lags 1 and 2 are large in absolute value, and exceed the significance bounds. The sample partial autocorrelations at higher lags are smaller, and lie within the significance bounds.

The partial correlogram suggests that the partial autocorrelations at lags 1 and 2 are non-zero, but provides little evidence that the partial correlations at higher lags are non-zero. Accordingly it is reasonable to conclude that $\alpha_2 \neq 0$ and $\alpha_k = 0$ for $k > 2$. Thus an AR(2) model might be appropriate for this time series.   ◆

Note the use of the word 'might' in the last sentence of Example 12.6: it is important to keep an open mind about what models may be appropriate. In particular, models other than an AR(2) model might fit the data equally well. Nevertheless, the partial correlogram provides a powerful tool in choosing a model. Activity 12.4 will give you some practice at using the partial correlogram in this way.

Activity 12.4   Choosing an autoregressive model for the dairy sales time series

In Example 12.1, a time series of daily sales of a dairy product was discussed. The time series appeared to be stationary, and its correlogram indicated marked departure from white noise. Figure 12.10 shows the partial correlogram for this time series.

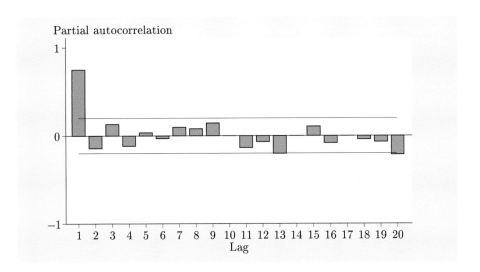

Figure 12.10   Partial correlogram for the dairy sales time series

The time series is to be modelled using an $AR(p)$ model. Suggest a suitable value of p. Explain your choice.

The following box summarizes the key features of autoregressive models.

Autoregressive models

Let X_t be a stationary time series with mean μ. The **autoregressive model of order p**, or **$AR(p)$** model, where p is a positive integer, has the following form:

$$X_t - \mu = \beta_1(X_{t-1} - \mu) + \cdots + \beta_p(X_{t-p} - \mu) + Z_t,$$

where $\beta_1, \ldots, \beta_p$ are parameters to be estimated, and Z_t is white noise with mean 0 and variance σ^2.

The ACF for an AR(1) model is given by $\rho_k = \beta_1^k$ for $k \geq 0$. The ACF for an $AR(p)$ model tails off exponentially in damped sinusoidal fashion with increasing lag.

The PACF for an $AR(p)$ model satisfies $\alpha_p = \beta_p$, and $\alpha_k = 0$ for lags $k > p$.

Summary of Section 12

In this section, autoregressive models for stationary time series have been introduced. The properties of autoregressive models of order 1 and of arbitrary order p have been described. The partial autocorrelation function PACF has been defined. The characteristics of the PACF for autoregressive models have been outlined. You have learned how to use the partial correlogram to choose the order of an autoregressive model.

Exercises on Section 12

Exercise 12.1   Autoregressive or not?

For each of the following time series models, state whether or not it is an autoregressive model. If your answer is no, explain why it is not an autoregressive model. If your answer is yes, state the order of the model. In each case, X_t is stationary with mean zero, and Z_t represents white noise.

(a) $X_t = 0.9X_{t-1} - 0.5X_{t-2} + Z_t$

(b) $X_t = -0.6X_{t-1} + 0.2X_{t-2} + 0.3X_{t-1}X_{t-2} + Z_t$

(c) $X_{t+1} = -0.2X_t + Z_{t+1}$

Exercise 12.2   Chemical process readings

In Activity 12.1, a time series of readings from a chemical process was described. The partial correlogram for this time series is shown in Figure 12.11.

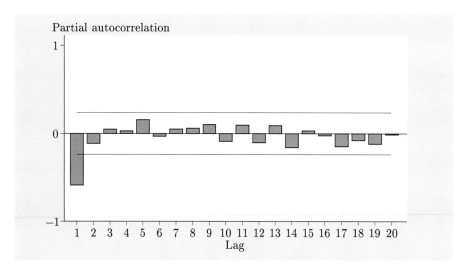

Figure 12.11   Partial correlogram for the chemical process data

(a) The time series is to be modelled using an autoregressive model. In your view, is this appropriate? If so, what is the order of the model? Give reasons for your answers.

(b) Assume that an AR(1) model is suitable. Use Figure 12.11 to obtain a rough estimate of the parameter β_1.

13   Moving average models

Autoregressive models are used to represent long-term dependence. For example, the autocorrelation function for an AR(1) model is given by $\rho_k = \beta^k$ for $k \geq 0$. For large lags, the autocorrelation is small, but non-zero, so a value observed a long time ago still exerts some influence over current and future values.

In this section, a family of models for stationary time series that can be used to represent short-term dependence is introduced. These are the moving average models. Like autoregressive models, moving average models are characterized by their order. In Subsection 13.1, the moving average model of order 1 is introduced. In Subsection 13.2, more general moving average models are described, and a method for choosing an appropriate moving average model is discussed.

13.1   The moving average model of order 1

Let X_t denote a stationary time series with zero mean. A model is required that can be used to represent short-term dependence between successive terms. Consider first the white noise model

$$X_t = Z_t,$$

where Z_t is a stationary time series of uncorrelated terms with mean zero and variance σ^2. The ACF for this model is zero at all lags $k \geq 1$, so for this model, there is no dependence at all between terms in the time series. Now consider the model

$$X_t = Z_t - \theta Z_{t-1},$$

where θ is a constant. Applying this model at time $t-1$ yields

$$X_{t-1} = Z_{t-1} - \theta Z_{t-2}.$$

You may wonder why $-\theta Z_{t-1}$ is used rather than $+\theta Z_{t-1}$: this is just a convention.

Since Z_{t-1} occurs both in the expression for X_t and in that for X_{t-1}, there is a non-zero correlation between X_t and X_{t-1}. For example, suppose that $\theta < 0$. In this case, if Z_{t-1} happens to be large and positive, then both X_t and X_{t-1} will tend to be large and positive. So there is a positive correlation between X_t and X_{t-1}. Applying the model again at time $t-2$ gives

$$X_{t-2} = Z_{t-2} - \theta Z_{t-3}.$$

The expression for X_{t-2} does not share any terms with the expression for X_t. Since the Z_t are uncorrelated, this means that the correlation between X_t and X_{t-2} is zero. Similarly, the correlation between X_t and X_{t-k} is zero for all $k \geq 2$. Thus the series X_t exhibits non-zero dependence only at lag 1, and hence the dependence is short-term.

This model for X_t is the **moving average model of order 1**, also written **MA(1)**. The MA(1) model is stationary whatever the value of θ. However, for technical reasons that will not be discussed here, the parameter θ is restricted to the range $-1 < \theta < 1$.

Moving averages were introduced in Section 4 as a way of smoothing a time series. The moving average *model* described here should not be confused with them.

The MA(1) model may be generalized to time series with non-zero mean; the definition is given in the following box.

Moving average model of order 1

Let X_t be a stationary time series with mean μ. The **moving average model of order 1**, or **MA(1)** model, has the following form:

$$X_t - \mu = Z_t - \theta Z_{t-1},$$

where θ is a parameter to be estimated, $-1 < \theta < 1$, and Z_t is white noise with mean 0 and variance σ^2.

As just explained, the autocorrelation function for the MA(1) model is zero at all lags greater than 1. In fact, it can be shown that the ACF is as follows:

$$\rho_1 = \frac{-\theta}{1 + \theta^2}, \tag{13.1}$$

$$\rho_k = 0 \quad \text{for } k > 1.$$

On the other hand, the partial autocorrelation function for the MA(1) model can be shown to decline exponentially in magnitude with increasing lag. If $\theta < 0$, the successive partial autocorrelations alternate in sign. If $\theta > 0$, the partial autocorrelations are negative at lags $k \geq 1$. Figure 13.1 shows the theoretical autocorrelation function and the theoretical partial autocorrelation function for lags 1 to 10 for MA(1) models with $\theta = 0.8$ and $\theta = -0.8$.

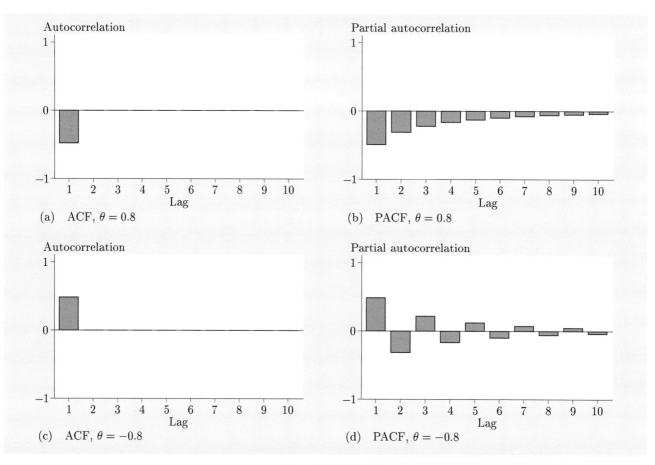

Figure 13.1 The ACF and the PACF for two MA(1) models

Note the duality between AR(1) and MA(1) models. In Section 12, you saw that for an AR(1) model, the ACF declines exponentially in magnitude and the PACF cuts off after lag 1. For an MA(1) model, the ACF cuts off after lag 1 and the PACF declines exponentially in magnitude. This duality can be exploited to choose a model for a time series, by examining the sample ACF and the sample PACF for the series.

Example 13.1 Annual changes in average temperature, 1901–2004

Most scientists are agreed that the climate of the Earth is changing. In the UK, annual average temperatures have increased over the last century. To analyse the rate of change of average temperatures, the annual change from year to year can be computed — that is, the average temperature in year t minus the average temperature in year $t - 1$. (This gives the time series of first differences of annual average temperatures.)

The time series of annual temperature changes between 1901 and 2004 in Central England is shown in Figure 13.2.

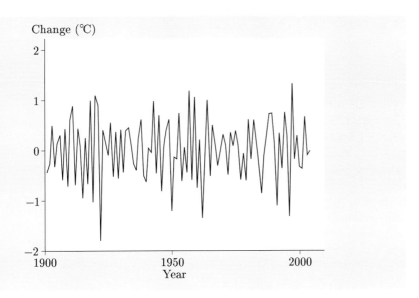

Figure 13.2   Time plot of annual changes in average temperature, 1901–2004

There is no clear trend or other systematic variation in the level or the size of the fluctuations, so the time series is stationary in mean and in variance. Thus there is no evidence to suggest that this time series is not stationary.

The correlogram and the partial correlogram for the time series are shown in Figure 13.3.

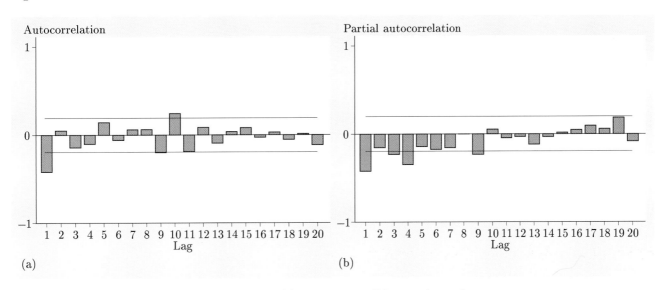

(a)   (b)

Figure 13.3   Changes in average temperature: (a) correlogram (b) partial correlogram

The correlogram in Figure 13.3(a) shows a clear negative autocorrelation at lag 1. Thereafter, the sample autocorrelations are smaller in magnitude and generally lie within the 95% significance bounds. There is one exception: the sample autocorrelation at lag 10 slightly exceeds the significance bound. Autocorrelations at higher lags are difficult to interpret, especially since one sample autocorrelation out of 20 could be expected to exceed the bounds by chance, even if the underlying autocorrelations were zero. Thus it is reasonable to ignore the autocorrelation at lag 10.

The partial correlogram shows negative values for the first few lags. The sample partial autocorrelations tend to decline in magnitude, though this pattern is by no means regular — for example, the values at lag 2 and lag 3 are smaller in magnitude than the value at lag 4.

It may therefore be concluded that the patterns in Figures 13.3(a) and 13.3(b) are broadly similar to those shown in Figures 13.1(a) and 13.1(b). Thus it is not unreasonable to interpret the patterns as suggestive of an MA(1) model, with the parameter θ taking a positive value.   ◆

In Example 13.1, a model was identified by comparing the sample ACF and sample PACF to the theoretical ACF and PACF. In fact, this is the standard way to choose a model. In making such comparisons, it is important to focus on the general features of the plots, and avoid being too fastidious about small differences between the sample and theoretical values. Activity 13.1 will give you some practice at identifying a model.

Activity 13.1   Variation in yield of Government securities

In this activity you will investigate the time series of monthly changes in the yield of British Government securities; increases in yield are positive, decreases are negative. This time series comprises the first differences of the time series of monthly yields, which was described in Example 11.4. Figure 13.4 shows the time plot for the time series of monthly changes, and Figure 13.5 shows the correlogram and the partial correlogram.

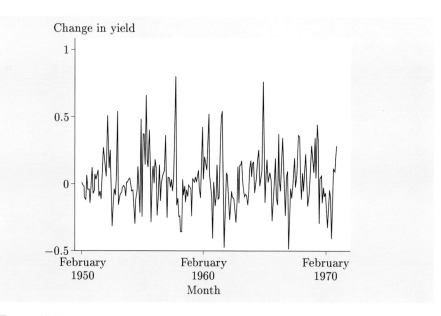

Figure 13.4   Time plot of monthly changes in yield

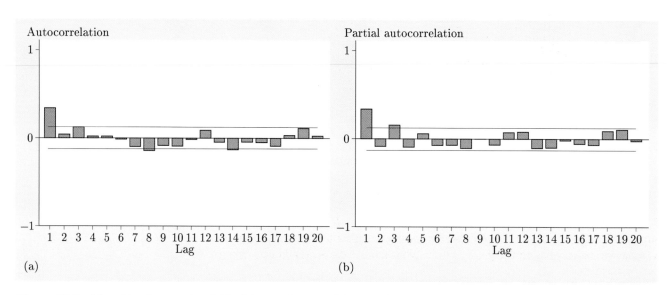

Figure 13.5   Monthly changes in yield: (a) correlogram (b) partial correlogram

(a) Is the time series stationary? Explain your answer. (You may assume that the time series is not seasonal.)

(b) It has been suggested that an MA(1) model is appropriate for this time series. Explain why this is a reasonable suggestion.

(c) Would you expect the value of the parameter θ to be positive or negative? Explain your answer.

13.2 The moving average model of order q

The moving average model of order 1 can be extended to include further terms. For example, the **moving average model of order 2**, or **MA(2)** model, for a stationary time series X_t with mean μ, has the following form:

$$X_t - \mu = Z_t - \theta_1 Z_{t-1} - \theta_2 Z_{t-2}, \tag{13.2}$$

where θ_1 and θ_2 are parameters to be estimated, and Z_t is white noise with mean zero and variance σ^2. As for the MA(1) model, for technical reasons some conditions are required on the parameters θ_1 and θ_2.

You may assume that all the models presented in this book satisfy these conditions.

Example 13.2 A simulated MA(2) time series

A time series was generated using the MA(2) model with $\mu = 16$, $\theta_1 = 0.6$, $\theta_2 = 0.2$ and $\sigma^2 = 2$. That is, values of independent normal random variables $Z_t \sim N(0, 2)$ were simulated and combined using the defining formula for the MA(2) model given in (13.2). The time plot for the first 100 values obtained is shown in Figure 13.6.

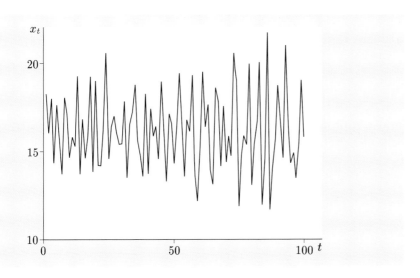

Figure 13.6 Time plot for 100 simulated values

The size of the fluctuations appears to increase slightly. However, the values were simulated using a model with constant variance, so this effect is due to chance. This serves to emphasize the general point that small effects should not be over-interpreted.

The correlogram and the partial correlogram are shown in Figure 13.7.

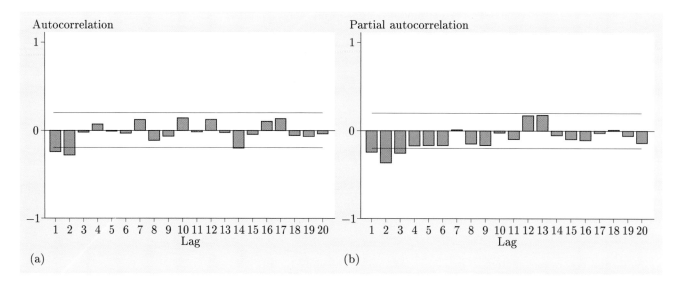

Figure 13.7   Simulated data: (a) correlogram (b) partial correlogram

The correlogram shows two (relatively) sizeable sample autocorrelations at lags 1 and 2. The sample autocorrelations at lags 3 to 20 are smaller in magnitude, and are generally contained within the significance bounds. Just one autocorrelation, at lag 14, peeps over the boundary. In fact, the underlying autocorrelation at lag 14 is known to be zero. This confirms that sample autocorrelations at higher lags should not be over-interpreted, unless there is good reason to suspect an effect.

In the partial correlogram, notice that the sample partial autocorrelations at the first few lags are negative, and the sample partial autocorrelations generally decline in magnitude after lag 2.

In general, the partial autocorrelation function for an MA(2) model either declines exponentially in magnitude, or exhibits a damped sinusoidal pattern (that is, alternating clumps of positive and negative values that tail off to zero in magnitude as the lag increases). The pattern in the partial correlogram in Figure 13.7(b) roughly matches the theoretical PACF for an MA(2) model.

The correlogram in Figure 13.7(a) displays sizeable sample autocorrelations only at lags 1 and 2. In fact, it can be shown that the theoretical autocorrelation function for an MA(2) model is non-zero at lag 2, and is zero at all lags $k > 2$ so the pattern in the correlogram is consistent with the theoretical ACF.   ◆

In general, for an MA(2) model,

$$\rho_2 = \frac{-\theta_2}{1 + \theta_1^2 + \theta_2^2},$$ (13.3)

$$\rho_k = 0 \quad \text{for } k > 2.$$

The ACFs for four MA(2) models are shown in Figure 13.8.

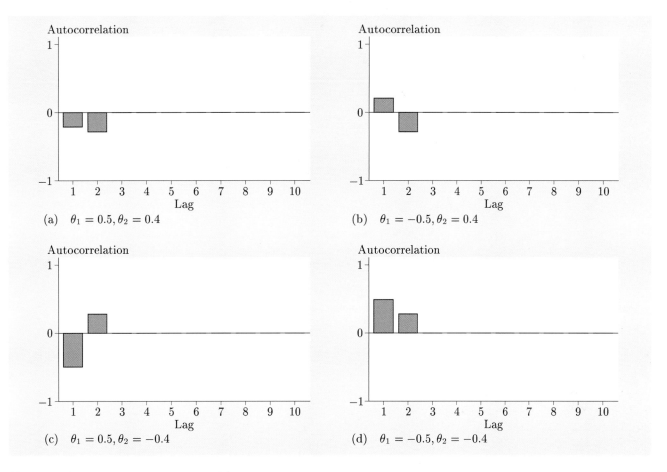

Figure 13.8   The ACFs for four MA(2) models

Notice that for each of these four MA(2) models, ρ_2 is non-zero and $\rho_k = 0$ for all $k > 2$.

The moving average model of order 1 may be extended to arbitrary order q, where q is a positive integer. The **moving average model of order q**, or **MA(q)** model, for a time series X_t with mean μ, has the following form:

$$X_t - \mu = Z_t - \theta_1 Z_{t-1} - \cdots - \theta_q Z_{t-q},$$

where $\theta_1, \theta_2, \ldots, \theta_q$ are constants, and Z_t is white noise with zero mean and variance σ^2. The autocorrelation function for an MA(q) model is non-zero at lag q, and zero at all lags $k > q$:

$$\rho_q = \frac{-\theta_q}{1 + \theta_1^2 + \cdots + \theta_q^2}, \tag{13.4}$$

$$\rho_k = 0 \quad \text{for } k > q.$$

Notice that when $q = 1$, Formula (13.4) reduces to Formula (13.1), and when $q = 2$, it is equivalent to Formula (13.3). So Formula (13.4) can be used to find the autocorrelation at lag q for an MA(q) model for any order $q \geq 1$.

The partial autocorrelation function tails off to zero in magnitude, either exponentially or in a damped sinusoidal pattern.

In Subsection 13.1, the ACFs and PACFs for MA(1) and AR(1) models were contrasted. Now consider the ACFs and PACFs for MA(q) and AR(p) models for general p and q. The autocorrelation function for an MA(q) model is non-zero at lag q and zero at all lags $k > q$, whereas the partial autocorrelation function tails off to zero in magnitude, either exponentially or in a damped sinusoidal pattern. In contrast, for an AR(p) model, the PACF cuts off after lag p and the ACF tails off to zero in magnitude. This difference is useful for choosing between a moving average model and an autoregressive model for a time series.

The definition and key properties of moving average models of order q are summarized in the following box.

Moving average models

Let X_t be a stationary time series with mean μ. The **moving average model of order q**, or **MA(q)** model, where q is a positive integer, has the following form:

$$X_t - \mu = Z_t - \theta_1 Z_{t-1} - \cdots - \theta_q Z_{t-q},$$

where $\theta_1, \ldots, \theta_q$ are parameters to be estimated, and Z_t is white noise with mean 0 and variance σ^2.

The ACF for an MA(q) model satisfies

$$\rho_q = \frac{-\theta_q}{1 + \theta_1^2 + \cdots + \theta_q^2},$$

$$\rho_k = 0 \quad \text{for } k > q.$$

The PACF for an MA(q) model tails off to zero in magnitude, either exponentially or in a damped sinusoidal pattern, as the lag increases.

Activity 13.2   Moving average models

Each of the expressions below represents a model for a stationary time series X_t with mean zero. In each case, Z_t is white noise. For each of the models, say whether or not it is a moving average model. If it is a moving average model, state the order q and calculate the autocorrelation at lag q. If it is not a moving average model, explain why not.

(a) $X_t = Z_t - 0.2Z_{t-1} + 0.3\sqrt{Z_{t-2}}$

(b) $X_t = Z_t - 0.5Z_{t-1} - 0.2Z_{t-2}$

(c) $X_t = 0.2X_{t-1} + Z_t - 0.1Z_{t-1}$

(d) $X_t = Z_t + 0.9Z_{t-1}$

Suppose that data $x_1, x_2, \ldots, x_n$ are available on a time series, and that the time plot suggests that the time series is stationary. If a moving average model is appropriate for the data, then the sample ACF and the sample PACF should roughly match the theoretical ACF and the theoretical PACF for the model. Matching the sample and the theoretical ACFs and PACFs in this way has been illustrated in Examples 13.1 and 13.2.

If a moving average model is appropriate, then the sample ACF should be close to zero after some lag q which defines the order of the model, and the sample PACF should tail off to zero with increasing lag. Activity 13.3 will give you some practice at deciding when a moving average model is appropriate, and choosing its order.

Activity 13.3   Choosing a moving average model

Figure 13.9 shows the time plot of the monthly percentage increase in seasonally adjusted electricity demand at a plant in California.

Delurgio, S.A. (1988) *Forecasting Principles and Applications.* McGraw-Hill, Singapore.

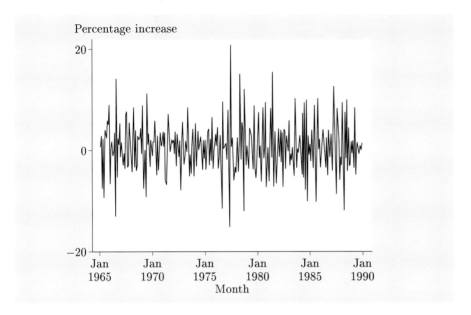

Figure 13.9   Percentage increase in seasonally adjusted electricity demand

The correlogram and partial correlogram for this time series are shown in Figure 13.10.

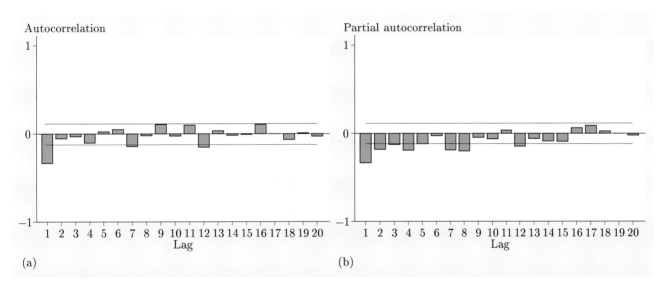

Figure 13.10   Percentage increase in seasonally adjusted electricity demand: (a) correlogram (b) partial correlogram

(a) Is this time series stationary? Explain your answer.

(b) It is suggested that this time series could be modelled using a moving average model. Identify two features of the time series that support this suggestion.

(c) What order would you choose for the model, and why?

Summary of Section 13

In this section, moving average models for stationary time series have been introduced. The properties of moving average models of order 1 and of arbitrary order q have been described. You have learned how to use the sample ACF and the sample PACF to decide whether a moving average model is appropriate and to choose its order.

Exercise on Section 13

Exercise 13.1   Identifying a moving average model

Figures 13.11 and 13.12 show the correlogram and the partial correlogram for two stationary time series.

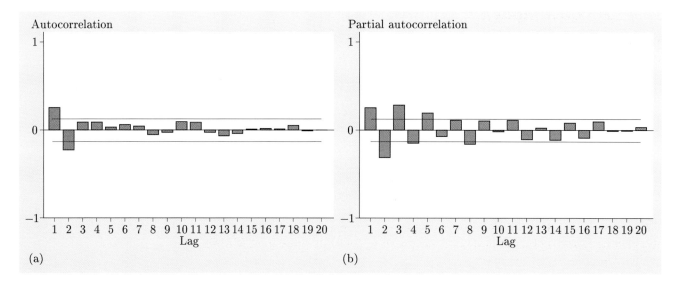

Figure 13.11   Time series 1: (a) correlogram (b) partial correlogram

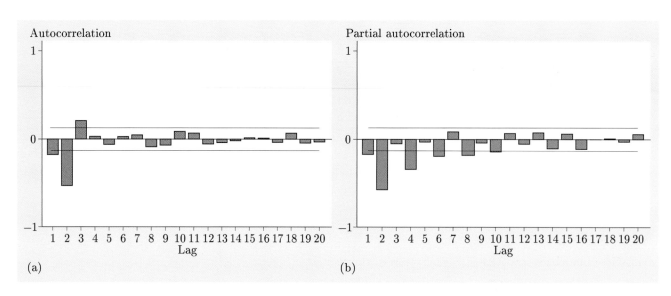

Figure 13.12   Time series 2: (a) correlogram (b) partial correlogram

For each of these two time series, decide whether or not a moving average model is appropriate. Explain your reasoning. If a moving average model is appropriate, choose the order of the model.

114

14 The ARIMA modelling framework

In Sections 12 and 13, autoregressive models and moving average models were introduced. In this section, a more general modelling framework is described, known as ARIMA modelling. This incorporates both autoregressive models and moving average models, and also allows for differencing of time series. You have already met most of the key ideas required: the main novelty of this section resides in how they all fit together.

ARIMA is pronounced 'ah-ree-mah'.

In Subsection 14.1, the ARIMA modelling framework is described. Then, in Subsection 14.2, you will learn how to choose an ARIMA model. Checking the adequacy of an ARIMA model is described in Subsection 14.3.

14.1 ARIMA models

As you may have suspected, the AR in ARIMA stands for autoregressive, and the MA for moving average. The I in the middle stands for Integrated (this is related to differencing). Thus an ARIMA model is an integrated autoregressive moving average model.

Suppose that X_t is a stationary time series with mean zero. The autoregressive model of order p, or AR(p) model, has the form

$$X_t = \beta_1 X_{t-1} + \cdots + \beta_p X_{t-p} + Z_t,$$

where Z_t is white noise with mean 0 and variance σ^2. This may be rewritten as

$$X_t - \beta_1 X_{t-1} - \cdots - \beta_p X_{t-p} = Z_t.$$

The term on the right-hand side is just white noise. A more general model is obtained by replacing this term by a moving average model of order q, or MA(q) model. Thus the model becomes

$$X_t - \beta_1 X_{t-1} - \cdots - \beta_p X_{t-p} = Z_t - \theta_1 Z_{t-1} - \cdots - \theta_q Z_{t-q}.$$

This may be rewritten as follows:

$$X_t = \beta_1 X_{t-1} + \cdots + \beta_p X_{t-p} + Z_t - \theta_1 Z_{t-1} - \cdots - \theta_q Z_{t-q}.$$

This is called the **autoregressive moving average model of order** (p, q), or **ARMA(p, q)** model. If $\beta_1 = \cdots = \beta_p = 0$, then the model reduces to an MA(q) model: the autoregressive term is said to be of order zero, and the model can be described as ARMA$(0, q)$. Similarly, if $\theta_1 = \cdots = \theta_q = 0$, then the moving average term is said to be of order zero, and the model can be described as ARMA$(p, 0)$: this coincides with the AR(p) model. If both $p = 0$ and $q = 0$, then the model is $X_t = Z_t$. Thus the ARMA$(0, 0)$ model is the white noise model.

Example 14.1   Some ARMA models

The model

$$X_t = 0.3 X_{t-1} + Z_t$$

is an AR(1) model, so it is ARMA$(1, 0)$. Similarly, the model

$$X_t = Z_t - 0.7 Z_{t-1} + 0.1 Z_{t-2}$$

is an MA(2) model, so it is ARMA$(0, 2)$. Combining these two models gives

$$X_t = 0.3 X_{t-1} + Z_t - 0.7 Z_{t-1} + 0.1 Z_{t-2}.$$

This is an autoregressive moving average model of order $(1, 2)$, or ARMA$(1, 2)$ model.   ♦

Activity 14.1   Classifying ARMA models

Identify the orders p and q of each of the following models, and hence classify each model using the ARMA(p,q) notation.

(a) $X_t = 0.3X_{t-1} - 0.1X_{t-2} + Z_t - 0.5Z_{t-1}$

(b) $X_t = Z_t - 0.9Z_{t-1}$

(c) $X_t = -0.2X_{t-1} + 0.3X_{t-2} - 0.1X_{t-3} + Z_t - 0.1Z_{t-1}$

For simplicity, it has been assumed that X_t has mean zero. If X_t has non-zero mean μ, then the general ARMA(p,q) model is obtained by substituting $(X_t - \mu)$ for X_t, $(X_{t-1} - \mu)$ for X_{t-1}, and so on.

It has also been assumed that X_t is stationary. In fact, many time series are not stationary, but can be differenced to obtain a stationary time series, as described in Section 11. The **order of differencing**, represented by the letter d, is the smallest number of times the series must be differenced to obtain a stationary time series. Once the time series has been differenced to produce stationarity, the ARMA(p,q) modelling framework can be used on the stationary time series.

An **integrated autoregressive moving average model of order** (p,d,q), or **ARIMA(p,d,q)** model, is an ARMA(p,q) model applied to a time series after differencing of order d. The reason why the model is called 'integrated' is explained in Example 14.2.

Example 14.2   Yield on British Government securities

Figure 14.1(a) shows the time plot of the monthly time series X_t of percentage yields on British Government securities.

This time series was introduced in Example 9.1.

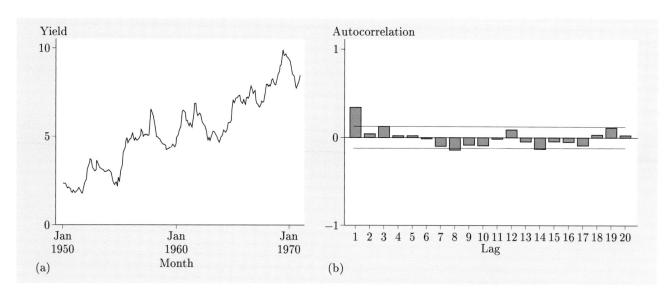

Figure 14.1   Percentage yield on British Government securities: (a) time plot (b) correlogram for first differences

This time series is clearly non-stationary. In Example 11.4, you saw that stationarity is obtained by differencing the series once. Hence the order of differencing for this time series is 1; that is, $d = 1$. Let Y_t denote the differenced series:

$$Y_t = X_t - X_{t-1}, \quad t = 2, 3, \ldots .$$

Note that

$$X_2 = (X_2 - X_1) + X_1 = Y_2 + X_1,$$
$$X_3 = (X_3 - X_2) + (X_2 - X_1) + X_1 = Y_3 + Y_2 + X_1.$$

More generally,

$$X_t = Y_t + Y_{t-1} + \cdots + Y_2 + X_1.$$

Thus the original time series X_t can be retrieved from the differenced series Y_t by summing the Y_t, and adding X_1 to the sum. Similarly, if an ARMA model for Y_t is available, then a model for X_t may be obtained by summing the models for $Y_t, Y_{t-1}, \ldots, Y_2$, and then adding X_1. The addition of successive terms of a time series is called **integration**. Thus the model for X_t is obtained by *integrating* the ARMA model for Y_t. This explains the letter I of ARIMA.

Figure 14.1(b) shows the sample ACF for Y_t, which you investigated in Activity 13.1. This suggests that an $\mathrm{ARMA}(0,1)$ model (that is, an MA(1) model) is appropriate for Y_t. This ARMA model for Y_t can then be integrated (that is, summed) to produce a model for the original time series X_t. The model for X_t is thus an *integrated* autoregressive moving average model of order $(0, 1, 1)$, or $\mathrm{ARIMA}(0, 1, 1)$ model. ◆

In Activity 13.1, you saw that an MA(1) model is appropriate for the time series of first differences.

In Example 14.2, a model for the original series X_t was obtained by integrating (that is, summing) the differenced series. The same idea applies whatever the order of differencing, the only difference being that successive integrations are required when $d \geq 2$. The details are omitted.

Activity 14.2   Classifying ARIMA models

In Example 11.5, the time series of the quarterly UK index of production was discussed. You saw that it is necessary to difference the series twice to obtain a stationary time series. Each of the following models is suitable for the twice-differenced series. Write down each model for the original series in the form $\mathrm{ARIMA}(p, d, q)$.

(a) An MA(1) model.

(b) An AR(2) model.

(c) The white noise model.

14.2   Selecting an ARIMA model

There are two main steps involved in selecting an ARIMA model. The first step is to obtain a stationary time series. Prior to differencing, the time series might need to be transformed — for instance, by taking logarithms — to ensure that it can be represented by an additive model, and hence is stationary in variance. Then the order of differencing, d, should be selected to ensure that the time series is stationary in mean. Transforming time series was introduced in Subsection 2.3, and differencing was described in Section 11.

It is assumed throughout that the time series is not seasonal.

Once a stationary time series has been obtained, the second step is to select an appropriate $\mathrm{ARMA}(p, q)$ model to represent it. The ARMA models you have met so far have all been either **purely autoregressive** — that is, AR(p) or $\mathrm{ARMA}(p, 0)$ — or **purely moving average** — that is, MA(q) or $\mathrm{ARMA}(0, q)$. However, the whole point of introducing the $\mathrm{ARMA}(p, q)$ notation is to allow models in which both p and q are non-zero. Such models combine an autoregressive component and a moving average component, and are called **mixed** ARMA models.

Example 14.3   An ARMA(1,1) model

A stationary time series X_t with mean $\mu = 5$ was simulated using the following ARMA$(1,1)$ model:

$$X_t - 5 = 0.6(X_{t-1} - 5) + Z_t + 0.9Z_{t-1},$$

where Z_t is white noise with mean zero and variance $\sigma^2 = 2$. The time plot of this time series is shown in Figure 14.2.

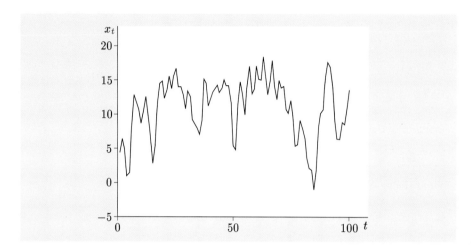

Figure 14.2   Time plot of simulated ARMA$(1,1)$ time series

Figure 14.3 shows the correlogram and the partial correlogram for this time series.

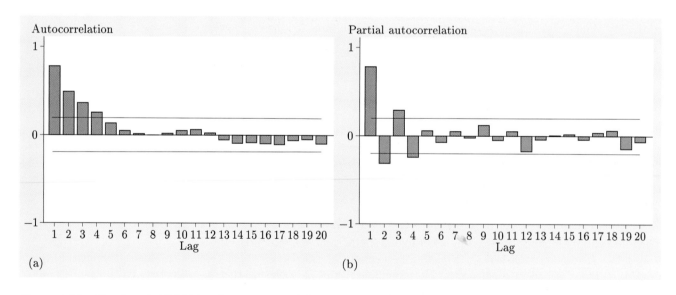

Figure 14.3   Simulated ARMA$(1,1)$ time series: (a) correlogram (b) partial correlogram

The sample autocorrelations shown in Figure 14.3(a) tail off gradually to zero, as would be expected for an autoregressive model. The partial correlogram in Figure 14.3(b) shows an alternating pattern, the magnitude of the sample partial autocorrelations also tailing off to zero gradually with increasing lag. This is what would be expected of a moving average model.   ◆

The patterns in the correlogram and the partial correlogram in Figure 14.3 are typical of the sample ACF and sample PACF for an ARMA$(1,1)$ time series. For an ARMA$(1,1)$ model, both the ACF and the PACF gradually tail off to zero, in either an exponential or damped sinusoidal manner. In fact, this is the case for all ARMA(p,q) models with $p > 0$ and $q > 0$: neither the ACF nor the PACF is zero after some lag. This makes distinguishing between such models difficult. In practice, most commonly used models have $p + q \leq 2$, so this is seldom a major problem.

Table 14.1 summarizes the key features of ARMA models, and is helpful in selecting an appropriate model.

Table 14.1   Notation and key features of ARMA models

Model	Notation	ACF	PACF
White noise	ARMA$(0,0)$	Zero at all lags	Zero at all lags
Autoregressive	ARMA$(p,0)$	Tails off to zero	Zero after lag p
Moving average	ARMA$(0,q)$	Zero after lag q	Tails off to zero
Mixed	ARMA(p,q)	Tails off to zero	Tails off to zero

This table refers only to lags $k \geq 1$. Recall that $\rho_0 = 1$ and $\alpha_0 = 1$.

Very often, more than one ARMA model may be appropriate for a given time series. A useful principle when selecting a model is to keep the value of $p + q$ to a minimum. This is called the **principle of parsimony**. This principle is illustrated in Example 14.4.

Example 14.4   The principle of parsimony

Suppose that the model used to generate the time series described in Example 14.3 is not known. How might you go about selecting a model, based on the correlogram and the partial correlogram shown in Figure 14.3?

Consulting Table 14.1, it is immediately clear that the white noise model is not appropriate, since several sample autocorrelations and sample partial autocorrelations exceed the significance bounds. However, other models are not ruled out by the properties of the ACF and PACF summarized in Table 14.1. A suitable justification for these other models might be as follows.

Autoregressive: the sample ACF tails off to zero, and the sample PACF is close to zero after lag 4. So an appropriate model is AR(4).

Moving average: the sample ACF is close to zero after lag 4, and the sample PACF tails off to zero. So an appropriate model is MA(4).

Mixed: both the sample ACF and sample PACF tail off to zero, so an appropriate model is ARMA(p,q) for p and q greater than or equal to 1.

Several models are therefore consistent with the properties given in Table 14.1. The next step is to work out how many parameters each of these various models has. The autoregressive part of the model has p parameters, $\beta_1, \ldots, \beta_p$. The moving average part of the model has q parameters, $\theta_1, \ldots, \theta_q$. According to the principle of parsimony, the model with the smallest total number of parameters $p + q$ should be selected.

Autoregressive AR(4): $p + q = 4 + 0 = 4$.

Moving average MA(4): $p + q = 0 + 4 = 4$.

Mixed ARMA$(1,1)$: $p + q = 2$. More generally, ARMA(p,q): $p + q$ parameters.

The model with the smallest value of $p + q$ among the plausible models is thus the mixed ARMA$(1,1)$ model. So this is the best candidate.   ◆

The principle of parsimony is not guaranteed to identify the best model, or even a good model. Rather, it is a useful 'rule of thumb' to help select an initial model, which you can then try out, and improve upon if it is found wanting. Invoking the principle of parsimony is only necessary if there are several likely candidate models. This may not always be the case: sometimes the classification in Table 14.1 determines a clear 'best' candidate. Activities 14.3 and 14.4 will give you some practice at choosing an appropriate ARIMA model.

Activity 14.3   ARIMA model for chemical concentrations

In Activity 4.2, the time series of concentration levels of a chemical process was introduced. The time plot for the concentrations, and the time plot for the first differences in concentrations, are shown in Figure 14.4.

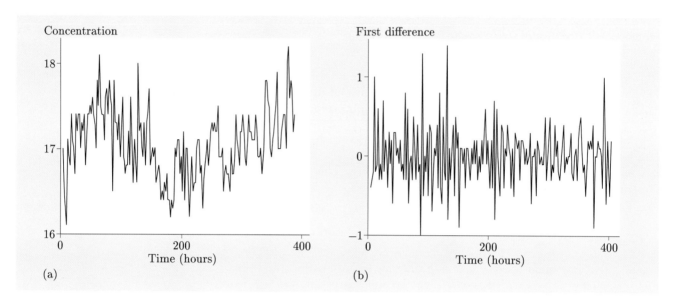

Figure 14.4   Chemical concentrations: (a) raw data (b) first differences

Figure 14.5 shows the correlogram and the partial correlogram for the first differences.

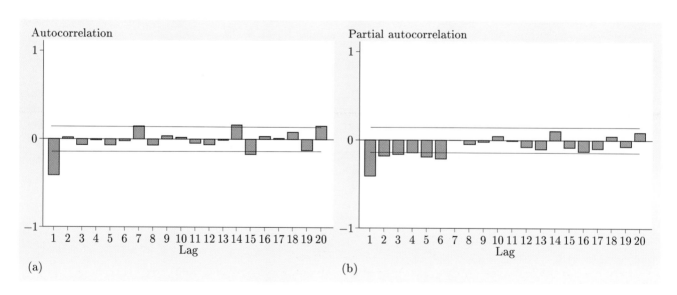

Figure 14.5   First differences of concentrations: (a) correlogram (b) partial correlogram

(a) Explain why d, the order of differencing required to obtain a stationary time series, is 1.

(b) Use Table 14.1 to identify a plausible model, and state why the other options are less plausible.

(c) Write down the model you chose in ARIMA(p, d, q) notation.

Activity 14.4   ARIMA models for the viscosity data

A time series of viscosity measurements was discussed in Examples 12.3 and 12.6. You saw that the time plot shown in Figure 12.5(a) suggests that the series is stationary. The correlogram for the time series is shown in Figure 12.5(b), and the partial correlogram in Figure 12.9.

(a) Use the correlogram and the partial correlogram to identify some plausible models for this time series. Explain your reasons.

(b) Use the principle of parsimony to identify one or two 'best' candidate models.

(c) List these models using the ARIMA(p, d, q) notation.

14.3   Fitting and checking the model

Once you have selected an ARIMA model, the next step is to estimate the parameters of the model, that is, to fit the model to the data. To fit the general ARIMA(p, d, q) model, the following parameters must be estimated.

◇   The mean of the series (after differencing, if applicable): μ.

◇   The p autoregressive parameters: $\beta_1, \ldots, \beta_p$.

◇   The q moving average parameters: $\theta_1, \ldots, \theta_q$.

◇   The standard deviation of Z_t: σ.

There are many ways of estimating the parameters of an ARIMA model. They will not be described in this book. The basic idea of these methods is to choose the parameter values in such a way that the 1-step ahead forecasts $\widehat{x}_t$ obtained using the fitted model are close to the observed values x_t, $t = 1, 2, \ldots, n$. One measure of closeness is the SSE, the sum of the squared forecast errors:

You will learn how to fit ARIMA models using SPSS in Section 15.

$$SSE = \sum_{t=1}^{n} e_t^2 = \sum_{t=1}^{n} (x_t - \widehat{x}_t)^2 \,.$$

1-step ahead forecasts, forecast errors and the SSE were introduced in Section 6.

The calculation of the 1-step ahead forecasts and the forecast errors is described in Example 14.5.

Example 14.5   1-step ahead forecasts and forecast errors for ARIMA models

Suppose that observations $x_1, x_2, \ldots, x_n$ are collected on a stationary time series X_t, and that 1-step ahead forecasts are required based on the ARIMA$(1, 0, 1)$ model

$$X_t = 0.6X_{t-1} + Z_t + 0.9Z_{t-1}.$$

First, choose the starting value: set $\widehat{x}_1 = 0$. Then the 1-step ahead forecast error at time $t = 1$ is

$$e_1 = x_1 - \widehat{x}_1 = x_1.$$

For $t = 2$, the model formula is $X_2 = 0.6X_1 + Z_2 + 0.9Z_1$. To obtain $\widehat{x}_2$, replace X_1 by the observed value x_1, replace Z_2 by its expected value, which is zero, and use e_1 to estimate Z_1. This gives

$$\widehat{x}_2 = 0.6x_1 + 0 + 0.9e_1.$$

At the next time point, $t = 3$, the model formula is $X_3 = 0.6X_2 + Z_3 + 0.9Z_2$. To obtain $\widehat{x}_3$, replace X_2 by x_2, replace Z_3 by its expected value (zero), and use $e_2 = x_2 - \widehat{x}_2$ to estimate Z_2. Thus

$$\widehat{x}_3 = 0.6x_2 + 0 + 0.9e_2.$$

The process is repeated in this way until the end of the series. A similar method is used for all ARIMA models.   ◆

An important point to note from Example 14.5 is that the 1-step ahead forecast error e_t is an estimate of Z_t. This may be used to check that the model is adequate, as follows. Since Z_t is white noise, if the model is adequate, then the time series of 1-step ahead forecast errors e_t (which estimate the Z_t) should be similar to white noise. In particular, the distribution of the forecast errors should be approximately normal with mean zero and constant variance, and the forecast errors should have zero autocorrelation.

The adequacy of the model may thus be checked in exactly the same way as described for exponential smoothing in Subsections 9.2 and 9.3. The steps involved are as follows.

◇   First, check that the distribution of the forecast errors is approximately normal with mean zero and constant variance. You can do this by examining a time plot and a histogram of the forecast errors.

◇   Then check that the autocorrelations of the forecast errors are zero at lags $k \geq 1$. This can be done by, for example, examining the correlogram for the forecast errors, and applying the Ljung–Box test for zero autocorrelation.

If the forecast errors are not white noise, then the model is not adequate. In this case, you will have to try a different model. If several plausible models have been identified, with the same value of $p + q$, then the SSE can be used to compare how well they fit the data: the model with the smallest SSE fits the data best. The method is illustrated in Example 14.6.

Example 14.6   Comparing and checking ARIMA models

In Activity 14.4, two plausible ARIMA models were identified for the viscosity data: an ARIMA$(2, 0, 0)$ model and an ARIMA$(1, 0, 1)$ model. These two models were fitted using a standard method.

For the fitted ARIMA$(2, 0, 0)$ model, the SSE was 1069.16, whereas for the ARIMA$(1, 0, 1)$ model, the SSE was 1114.91. Thus the ARIMA$(2, 0, 0)$ model fits the data better than the ARIMA$(1, 0, 1)$ model.

The time plot of the original data and the 1-step ahead forecasts obtained using the ARIMA$(2, 0, 0)$ model are shown in Figure 14.6.

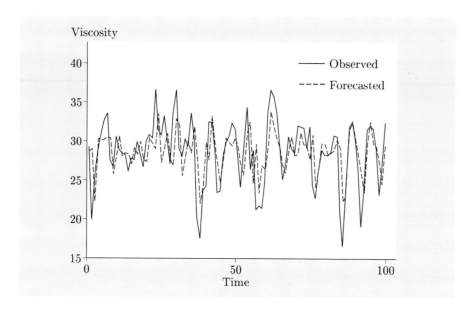

Figure 14.6   Viscosity data: observed values and 1-step ahead forecasts

To verify that the model is adequate, we must first check that the forecast errors are approximately normally distributed about zero with constant variance. The time plot and a histogram of the forecast errors are shown in Figure 14.7.

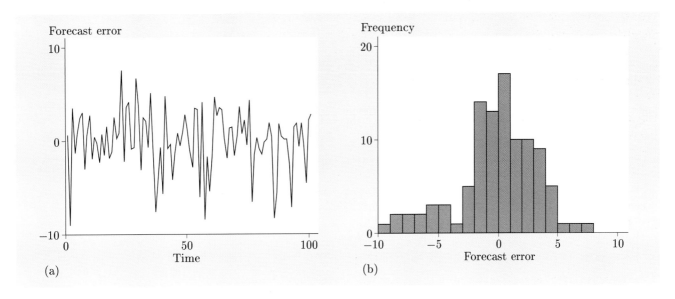

Figure 14.7   Forecast errors: (a) time plot (b) histogram

From the time plot in Figure 14.7(a), the forecast errors fluctuate around zero, and the fluctuations do not vary in magnitude. Hence it is reasonable to assume that they have mean zero and constant variance. From the histogram in Figure 14.7(b), it appears that the normality assumption is just about tenable. However, there is a suggestion that the forecast errors might be negatively skewed, because of the long left tail on the histogram. Nevertheless, the normality assumption is not unreasonable.

The next step is to check that the autocorrelations are zero. Figure 14.8 shows the correlogram for the forecast errors.

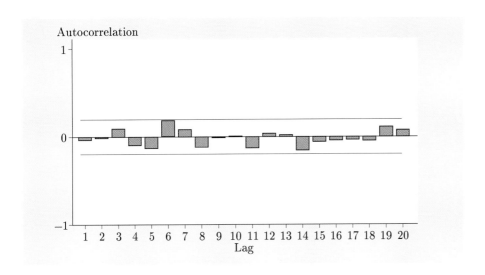

Figure 14.8   Correlogram for the forecast errors

The correlogram does not suggest that there are any non-zero autocorrelations at lags 1 to 20. This is confirmed by the Ljung–Box test for zero autocorrelation at lags 1 to 20. The value of the test statistic is 17.946, and the p value is 0.59. Hence there is little evidence against the null hypothesis that all autocorrelations at lags 1 to 20 are zero.

In conclusion, it appears that the $\text{ARIMA}(2,0,0)$ model has adequately accounted for the correlation structure within this time series.   ♦

123

Activity 14.5 will give you some practice at evaluating the adequacy of an
ARIMA model.

Activity 14.5   An ARIMA model for the British Government securities data

The time series of monthly yields on British Government securities was
introduced in Example 9.1. In Example 11.4, you saw that the series of first
differences appears to be stationary; and in Activity 13.1, an MA(1) model was
suggested as a reasonable model for the first differences. This suggests that the
original data might be modelled using an ARIMA$(0, 1, 1)$ model. Figure 14.9
shows the time plot of observed and fitted values (that is, the 1-step ahead
forecasts), and the time plot, a histogram and the correlogram for the forecast
errors obtained using an ARIMA$(0, 1, 1)$ model.

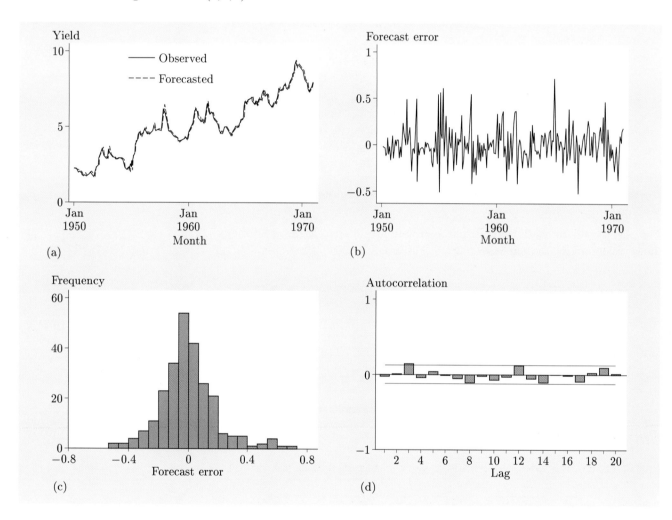

Figure 14.9   ARIMA model for securities data: (a) observed values and 1-step ahead forecasts (b) time plot of
forecast errors (c) histogram of forecast errors (d) correlogram for forecast errors

The value of the Ljung–Box test statistic for lags 1 to 20 is 24.16, and the p value
is 0.24. Discuss whether an ARIMA$(0, 1, 1)$ model is adequate for these data.

In Section 9, Holt's exponential smoothing method was used to obtain 1-step ahead forecasts for the time series of yields on British Government securities discussed in Activity 14.5. In Activity 9.4, you examined the correlogram for the forecast errors: the correlogram shows that the forecast errors are correlated (as the autocorrelation at lag 1 is clearly non-zero). Thus Holt's exponential smoothing method is not optimal for the time series, as the forecast errors obtained are not uncorrelated. On the other hand, the $\text{ARIMA}(0, 1, 1)$ model accounts for the underlying correlation structure of the time series. In this sense, the ARIMA model is an improvement over exponential smoothing for this time series.

The steps involved in selecting and checking the adequacy of an ARIMA model are summarized in the following box.

Selecting and checking an ARIMA model

The steps involved in selecting an ARIMA model for a non-seasonal time series are as follows.

◇   Check that an additive model is appropriate for the time series. If it is not appropriate, transform the time series to obtain a series that can be represented by an additive model.

◇   Identify the order of differencing, d, required to obtain stationarity.

◇   Identify those $\text{ARIMA}(p, d, q)$ models that are consistent with the correlogram and the partial correlogram for the stationary series.

◇   Choose the model(s) with the lowest value of $p + q$.

After fitting an ARIMA model, its adequacy should be checked, as follows.

◇   Check the fit of the model by examining a multiple time plot of the time series and the 1-step ahead forecasts.

◇   Verify that the distribution of the forecast errors is approximately normal with mean zero and constant variance.

◇   Use the correlogram for the forecast errors and the Ljung–Box test to check that the forecast errors are uncorrelated.

More general ARIMA models are available for seasonal time series. Although they do not involve any essentially new ideas, they are more complicated and are not covered in this book.

Summary of Section 14

In this section, integrated autoregressive moving average models have been described, and the $\text{ARIMA}(p, d, q)$ notation has been introduced. You have learned how to classify ARIMA models, and how to select ARIMA models for a time series, making use of the principle of parsimony. You have learned how to check the adequacy of an ARIMA model by inspecting the 1-step ahead forecasts and the forecast errors from the model.

Exercises on Section 14

Exercise 14.1   Classifying ARIMA models

The descriptions that follow relate to ARIMA models for a time series X_t.
Identify the values of p, d and q from these descriptions, and hence describe them
using ARIMA(p, d, q) notation.

(a) After twice differencing the series X_t, an autoregressive model of order 2 was
fitted.

(b) X_t is a stationary time series with mean zero, and

$$X_t = 0.3X_{t-1} + Z_t - 0.2Z_{t-1} + 0.1Z_{t-2},$$

where Z_t is white noise.

(c) An ARMA$(1, 1)$ model was fitted to the series of first differences of X_t.

(d) Y_t is stationary, and

$$Y_t - \mu = Z_t + 0.4Z_{t-1},$$

where $Y_t = X_t - X_{t-1}$ and Z_t is white noise.

Exercise 14.2   Selecting an ARIMA model

The correlogram and the partial correlogram for a stationary time series are
shown in Figure 14.10.

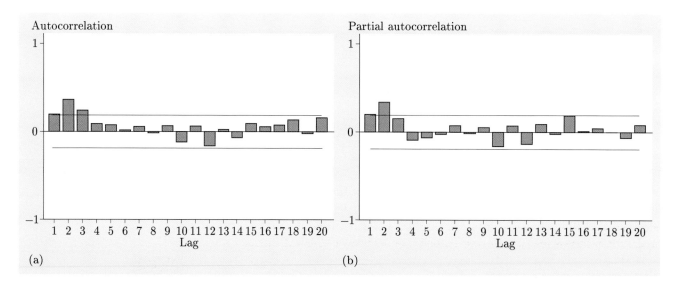

Figure 14.10   A stationary time series: (a) correlogram (b) partial correlogram

(a) It is proposed to model this time series using an autoregressive model. Is this
reasonable? Choose an appropriate value for p.

(b) Now suppose it is suggested that a moving average model is used. Is this
reasonable? Choose an appropriate value for q.

(c) Finally, it is suggested that an ARMA$(1, 1)$ model is used. Do you think this
is reasonable? Explain your answer.

(d) From the models suggested in parts (a), (b) and (c), select a shortlist of
models using the principle of parsimony.

Exercise 14.3   Checking model adequacy

An MA(1) model is fitted to the data used in Exercise 14.2. Figure 14.11 shows a histogram and the correlogram for the forecast errors.

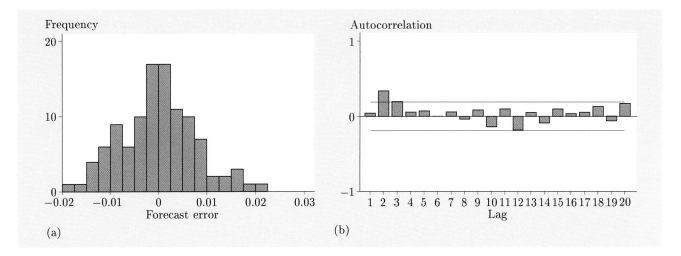

Figure 14.11   Forecast errors from an MA(1) model: (a) histogram (b) correlogram

The p value for the Ljung–Box test at lags 1 to 20 is 0.01. Is an MA(1) model adequate for this time series? Explain your reasoning.

15   ARIMA modelling in SPSS

In this section, you will learn how to use SPSS to select, fit and check the adequacy of ARIMA models. You will also learn how to obtain forecasts and prediction intervals for these forecasts, based on a suitable ARIMA model.

Refer to Chapter 8 of Computer Book 2 for the work in this section.

Summary of Section 15

In this section, you have learned how to use SPSS to obtain the correlogram and partial correlogram for a time series, if necessary after differencing. Fitting ARIMA models in SPSS has been described, along with checking model adequacy. You have learned how to obtain forecasts one or more steps ahead, and prediction limits for these forecasts.

16 Exercises on Book 2

Exercise 16.1 Sunspots data

Sunspots appear on the surface of the Sun as dark blotches. The number and size of sunspots, and the pattern of their appearance, has fascinated scientists and amateur astronomers for centuries. A famous data set tracks monthly sunspot activity, as measured by the 'sunspot number', since January 1749. Figure 16.1 shows the time plot of the monthly sunspot numbers between January 1934 and December 1983, a span of 50 years.

The complete data set may be obtained from the Datasets Archive of the StatLib Index at http://lib.stat.cmu.edu/datasets/Andrews.

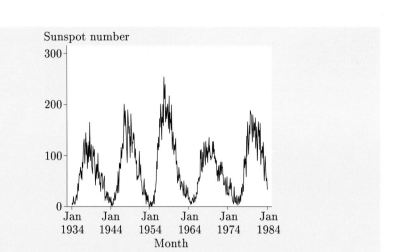

Figure 16.1 Sunspot number, 1934–1983

(a) Describe the main features of this time series, and obtain a rough estimate of the period T of the cycle.

(b) Is an additive model with a cyclical component likely to be appropriate for these data? Explain your reasoning.

An additive model with a cyclical component is similar to an additive model with annual seasonality, except that the cycle has period T rather than period one year.

The time plots for two transformations of the time series of sunspot numbers are shown in Figure 16.2.

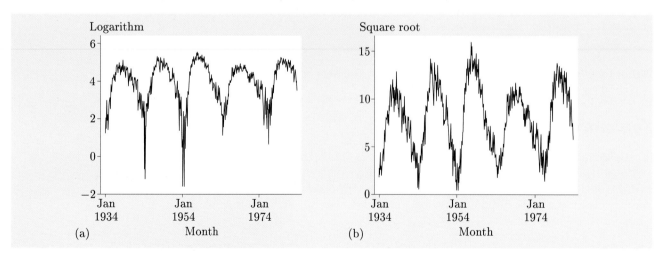

Figure 16.2 Transformed sunspot numbers: (a) logarithms (b) square roots

(c) Which transformation yields a time series that may be described adequately by an additive model? Explain your answer.

128

Exercise 16.2   *Maximum temperatures in Alaska*

Figure 16.3 shows the time plot of the *maximum* temperature (in degrees Fahrenheit) recorded each month in Anchorage, Alaska, between January 1954 and December 2004.

These data were obtained in July 2005 from the website http://climate.gi.alaska.edu.

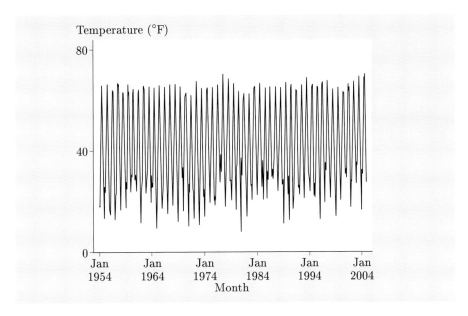

Figure 16.3   Maximum monthly temperatures (°F) in Anchorage, Alaska

(a) Describe the main features of this time plot.

(b) A decomposition of the time series yields the estimated seasonal factors shown in Table 16.1.

Table 16.1   Estimated seasonal factors

Month j	$\widehat{s}_j$
January	−21.21
February	−16.79
March	−10.05
April	0.55
May	11.91
June	19.35
July	22.26
August	20.24
September	12.13
October	−2.61
November	−15.16
December	−20.64

Explain briefly how these estimates are obtained. Interpret the seasonal factors.

One of the plots in Figure 16.4 is the time plot of the seasonally adjusted maximum temperatures. Simple moving averages of orders 11, 51 and 121 were used to obtain three estimates of the trend component. The time plots of these trend estimates are also shown in Figure 16.4.

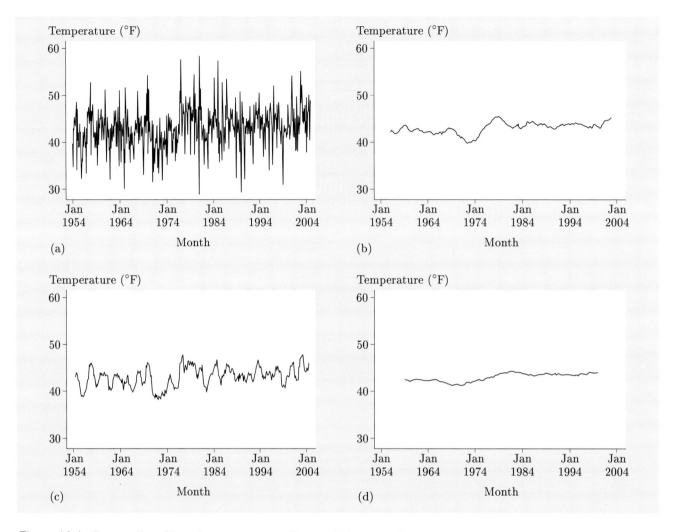

Figure 16.4   Seasonally adjusted temperatures: data and three moving averages

(c)   Which of the plots is the time plot of the seasonally adjusted series? Which moving average was used to produce each of the other three time plots? Give a reason for your answer.

(d)   In your view, which of the three moving averages produces the best estimate of the trend? Explain your choice.

(e)   Use the time plot for the moving average you chose in part (d) to describe the underlying trend in maximum temperatures.

Exercise 16.3   Forecasting the Dow Jones index

The Dow Jones industrial average is an index based on share prices of leading companies. It is used to chart movements on the New York Stock Exchange. Figure 16.5 shows the time plot of the logarithms of the closing values of the Dow Jones index on the last day of each month between January 1988 and June 2005.

These data were obtained in July 2005 from http://uk.finance.yahoo.com.

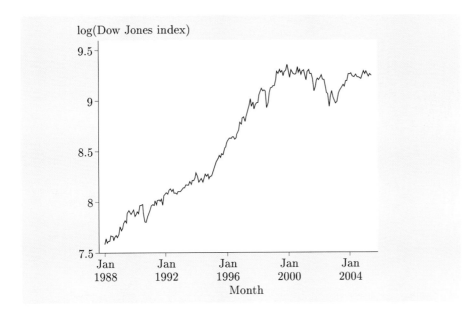

Figure 16.5   Time plot of the logarithms of the Dow Jones index

(a) Describe the main features of the time plot. Is an additive model appropriate for these data?

(b) It is required to forecast the July 2005 value using an exponential smoothing method, applied to data from January 2000. Identify an appropriate method, and explain your choice. (The seasonal variation in this time series is small and may be ignored.)

(c) The first few values from January 2000 are shown in Table 16.2.

Table 16.2   Dow Jones index, January 2000–April 2000

Date	Dow Jones index
January 2000	10 940.53
February 2000	10 128.31
March 2000	10 921.92
April 2000	10 733.91

The simple exponential smoothing method is to be applied to the logarithms of the Dow Jones index from January 2000. Choose an appropriate starting value.

(d) Table 16.3 shows the SSE for several values of the smoothing parameter α for the simple exponential smoothing method.

Identify the optimal value of the parameter α. Interpret this value in terms of the relative weight given to observations in the recent past and the more distant past.

(e) The observed value of the logarithm of the Dow Jones index for June 2005 was 9.2375, and the 1-step ahead forecast for June 2005 is 9.2537. Use these values to obtain a 1-step ahead forecast for the July 2005 value of the Dow Jones index.

Table 16.3   Smoothing parameter α and SSE

α	SSE
0.0	1.2421
0.1	0.3921
0.2	0.2545
0.3	0.1982
0.4	0.1694
0.5	0.1527
0.6	0.1426
0.7	0.1366
0.8	0.1335
0.9	0.1328
1.0	0.1342

Exercise 16.4   *Prediction limits for the Dow Jones index*

Holt's exponential smoothing method was applied to the time series of logarithms of the Dow Jones index for the period January 1988 to June 2005.

Figure 16.6 shows the time plot and a histogram of the 1-step ahead forecast errors.

The Dow Jones index was described in Exercise 16.3.

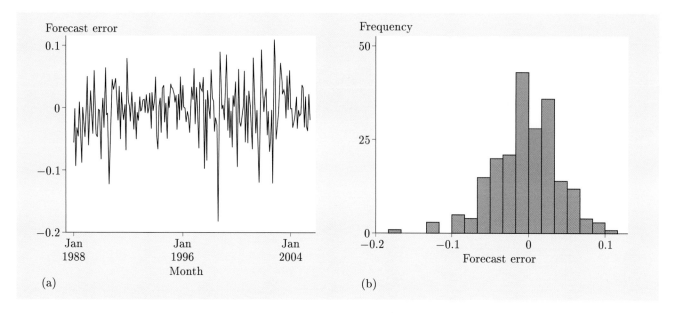

Figure 16.6   Forecast errors for Holt's method: (a) time plot (b) histogram

(a) Discuss whether it is reasonable to assume that the forecast errors are normally distributed with mean zero and constant variance.

Figure 16.7 shows the correlogram for the forecast errors, at lags 1 to 20.

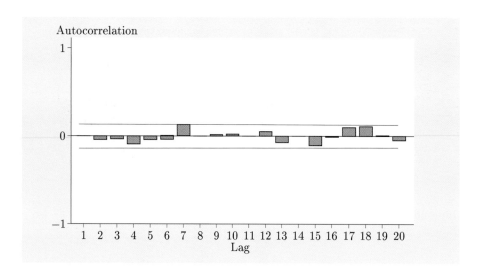

Figure 16.7   Correlogram for the forecast errors

(b) The length of the time series is 210. Calculate the 95% significance bounds, and interpret the correlogram. Is it reasonable to conclude that the forecast errors are white noise? Explain your answer.

(c) The *SSE* is 0.3925, and the 1-step ahead forecast of the logarithm of the Dow Jones index for July 2005 is 9.2407. Obtain the July 2005 forecast for the Dow Jones index, and a 95% prediction interval.

Exercise 16.5   A model for the Dow Jones index

A time plot of the first differences of the Dow Jones index for the period
January 1988 to June 2005 is shown in Figure 16.8.

The Dow Jones index was
described in Exercise 16.3.

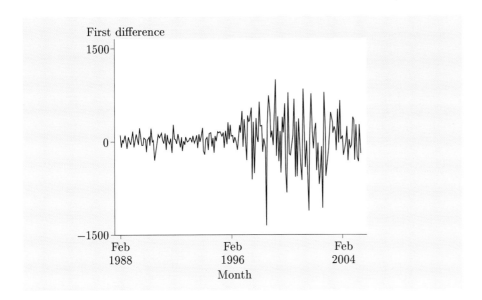

Figure 16.8   Time plot of first differences of the Dow Jones index

(a) You may assume that the Dow Jones index is not seasonal. Is the time series
in Figure 16.8 stationary? Explain your answer.

Time plots of the first differences and the second differences of the logarithm of
the Dow Jones index are shown in Figure 16.9.

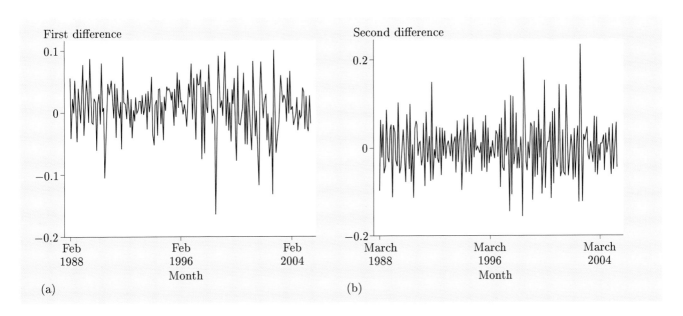

Figure 16.9   Logarithms of the Dow Jones index: (a) first differences (b) second differences

(b) Using these plots, and the time plot shown in Figure 16.5, identify the order
of differencing d of the logarithms of the Dow Jones index required to
produce a stationary time series.

133

Figure 16.10 shows the correlogram and the partial correlogram for the first differences of the logarithms of the Dow Jones index.

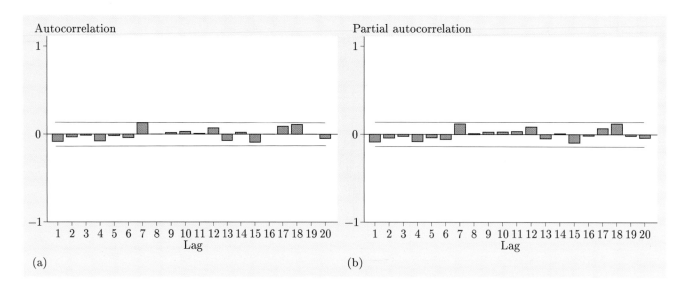

(a)   (b)

Figure 16.10   First differences of log Dow Jones index: (a) correlogram (b) partial correlogram

(c)   Interpret the correlogram and the partial correlogram.

(d)   Identify a plausible model for the logarithms of the Dow Jones index, and express this model in ARIMA(p, d, q) notation.

Exercise 16.6   *Models for the maximum monthly temperatures*

The time series of maximum monthly temperatures (in °F) recorded in Anchorage, Alaska, between January 1954 and December 2004 was described in Exercise 16.2. This exercise is based on the seasonally adjusted time series, which is shown in Figure 16.4(a).

The correlogram and partial correlogram for the seasonally adjusted data are shown in Figure 16.11.

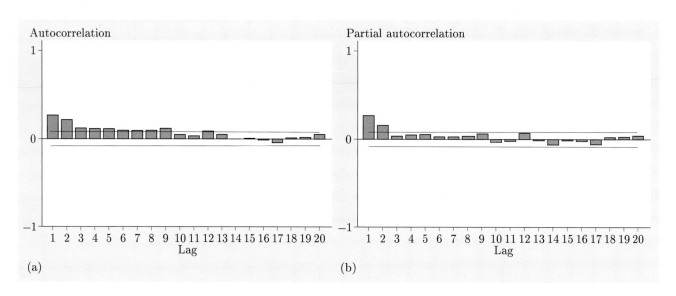

(a)   (b)

Figure 16.11   Seasonally adjusted maximum temperatures: (a) correlogram (b) partial correlogram

(a)   Suggest one or more plausible ARIMA models, justifying your choice in each case.

In Exercise 16.2, it was suggested that the level of the series may have increased slightly over the period. Accordingly, the series of first differences of the seasonally adjusted data were obtained. The correlogram and the partial correlogram for the first differences are shown in Figure 16.12.

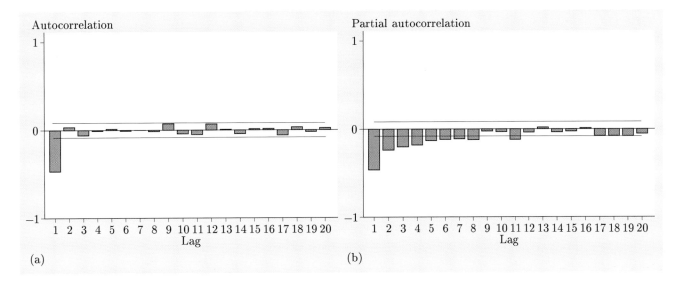

Figure 16.12 First differences of seasonally adjusted maximum temperatures: (a) correlogram (b) partial correlogram

(b) It is proposed to fit an $ARIMA(0, 1, 1)$ model. Explain why this is a reasonable suggestion.

(c) The estimated parameters of the $ARIMA(0, 1, 1)$ model are $\widehat{\mu} = 0.007$, $\widehat{\theta} = 0.865$ and $\widehat{\sigma} = 4.042$. Write down the model formula for the first differences.

(d) Two models are fitted to the seasonally adjusted data: an $ARIMA(2, 0, 0)$ model and an $ARIMA(0, 1, 1)$ model. Table 16.4 shows the p values obtained for the Ljung–Box test of zero autocorrelation of the forecast errors at lags 1 to 20.

Briefly discuss the relative merits of the two models. What other information might you require?

Table 16.4 p values for Ljung–Box test

Model	p value
$ARIMA(2, 0, 0)$	0.541
$ARIMA(0, 1, 1)$	0.003

Summary of Book 2

Part I

Time series are observations made at equally-spaced times. A time plot may be used to identify the main features of a time series; these may include the trend, seasonal variation and irregular fluctuations. Decomposition models are used to represent time series in terms of these components. Additive decomposition models, in which the components are added, play a central role in time series analysis. Visual inspection of the time plot for a series can help determine whether an additive decomposition model is appropriate, or whether the time series may need to be transformed. The trend component of a non-seasonal time series may be estimated by smoothing the time series using a moving average. The order of the moving average is chosen so as to avoid either under-smoothing the series or over-smoothing it. For a seasonal time series, a weighted moving average can be used to estimate the seasonal component of the time series, and hence obtain a seasonally adjusted series.

Part II

Forecasting is a central preoccupation of time series analysis. A simple forecasting method for non-seasonal time series with constant level is simple exponential smoothing. The forecasts depend on a single smoothing parameter; the value of this parameter may be chosen so as to minimize the sum of squared errors. More elaborate versions of exponential smoothing, namely Holt's method for time series with a linear trend, and the Holt–Winters method for seasonal time series, are also available. However, all forecasting methods rest upon the untestable assumption that the past is a good guide to the future. Assuming this to be the case, the accuracy of the forecasts can be quantified using prediction limits. Their calculation rests upon the assumption that the forecast errors are white noise. This may be checked by examining the distribution of the forecast errors and their correlogram, and by testing for zero autocorrelation using the Ljung–Box portmanteau test.

Part III

Models that account for the correlation structure of a time series may help to improve upon exponential smoothing methods. These models are defined for stationary series. Stationarity may be obtained by differencing the series appropriately. Autoregressive models allow for long-term dependence between the successive terms of a time series. In contrast, moving average models allow for short-term dependence. Both types of models are characterized by their order. The order of an autoregressive model may be identified from its partial autocorrelation function, while the order of a moving average model may be identified from its autocorrelation function. Autoregressive and moving average models for a differenced non-seasonal time series may be combined, resulting in an ARIMA(p, d, q) model. An appropriate ARIMA model for a given time series may be selected by examining the correlogram and partial correlogram for the series, and applying the principle of parsimony to select the simplest plausible model. The adequacy of this model may then be investigated by checking that the forecast errors are white noise, as for exponential smoothing. ARIMA models can readily be used to obtain forecasts and prediction intervals.

Learning outcomes

You have been working to develop the following skills.

Part I

◇   Represent time series data using time plots and seasonal plots.

◇   Interpret time plots and seasonal plots.

◇   Describe the trend component, the seasonal component and the irregular component of a time series.

◇   Decide whether an additive decomposition model is appropriate for a time series, after transformation if necessary.

◇   Estimate the trend component of a non-seasonal time series using a moving average.

◇   Choose the order of a moving average for trend estimation.

◇   Describe the estimation of the seasonal, trend and irregular components of a seasonal time series that can be described by an additive decomposition model.

◇   Describe the calculation of a seasonally adjusted series.

◇   Interpret estimated seasonal factors and trends.

◇   Use SPSS to enter and plot time series data and to undertake decompositions.

Part II

◇   Obtain 1-step ahead forecasts using simple exponential smoothing.

◇   Decide when it is appropriate to use simple, Holt's or Holt–Winters exponential smoothing.

◇   Interpret the results obtained using exponential smoothing methods.

◇   Choose values for the smoothing parameters for an exponential smoothing method.

◇   Assess the accuracy of forecasts using the sum of squared errors.

◇   Be aware of the assumptions underlying forecasting methods.

◇   Represent and interpret sample autocorrelations using the correlogram.

◇   Calculate and interpret significance bounds for sample autocorrelations.

◇   Test the null hypothesis of zero autocorrelation using the Ljung–Box test.

◇   Calculate approximate prediction intervals for 1-step ahead forecasts.

◇   Check the white noise assumption required for calculating prediction intervals.

◇   Use SPSS to apply exponential smoothing methods.

Part III

◇   Identify whether a time series is stationary in mean and in variance.

◇   Obtain a stationary time series from a non-stationary one by differencing.

◇   Interpret the correlogram and the partial correlogram for a time series.

◇   Use the correlogram and partial correlogram for a time series to select possible ARIMA models.

◇   Describe the structure of an $ARIMA(p, d, q)$ model.

◇   Classify an ARIMA model given its model formula.

◇   Choose an ARIMA model using the principle of parsimony.

◇   Check the adequacy of an ARIMA model.

◇   Use SPSS to select, fit and check the adequacy of an ARIMA model.

◇   Use SPSS to obtain forecasts from an ARIMA model.

Solutions to Activities

Solution 1.1

(a) In general, the number of visits overseas seems to be increasing from year to year.

(b) There seems to be a peak each year between June and September, and a trough between December and February.

Solution 1.2

(a) The increasing trend appears to steepen over time, so it is not linear. Perhaps it is roughly quadratic or exponential.

(b) The size of the seasonal fluctuations appears to increase over time.

Solution 1.3

There is a marked cyclic pattern of successive highs and lows in these data, which is probably attributable to seasonal variation. There may also be a downward trend, though this is harder to detect owing to the large fluctuations in the data.

Solution 1.4

(a) The time plot includes three complete cycles. Each cycle includes two peaks: a high peak (in which the blood pressure reaches about 120) and a lower peak.

(b) The high peaks occur at about 530, 1150 and 1790 milliseconds, so the period is between 600 and 650 milliseconds.

Solution 2.1

(a) The seasonal factors should repeat at intervals of 4, but $s_1 = -2$ and $s_5 = s_{1+4} = -3$. So this sequence does not represent the seasonal component.

(b) For this sequence, $s_t = s_{t+4}$ and $s_1 + s_2 + s_3 + s_4 = 0$, so it represents the seasonal component.

(c) For this sequence, $s_1 + s_2 + s_3 + s_4 = -4 + 3 + 3 - 1 = 1 \neq 0$, so it does not represent the seasonal component.

Solution 2.2

For the time series of overseas visits, the size of the seasonal fluctuations increases as the level of the time series increases. Thus an additive model is not appropriate for this time series.

Since the time series of annual average temperatures is non-seasonal, there are no seasonal fluctuations. The level of the time series increases between 1951 and 2004, but the irregular fluctuations do not appear to vary in size with the level. Thus an additive model may be appropriate for this time series.

Solution 2.3

(a) The seasonal fluctuations for the log transformed series decrease in size as the level increases. Hence an additive model is not appropriate for the log transformed series.

(b) From part (a), it follows that a multiplicative model is not appropriate for the time series of monthly visits overseas. In Activity 2.2, you found that an additive model is not appropriate for the time series. Hence neither an additive model nor a multiplicative model is appropriate for the time series.

Solution 2.4

(a) The size of the seasonal fluctuations is roughly the same, irrespective of the underlying level of the time series: the seasonal fluctuations are about the same size at the beginning of the series as they are at the end of the series, when the level is lower. On the other hand, the fluctuations of the irregular component may be greater at the end of the series than at the beginning.

(b) The square root transformation also reduces the variability in the size of the seasonal fluctuations, though perhaps not quite as successfully as the log transformation. On the other hand, the irregular fluctuations do not appear to vary in size with the level of the series.

(c) Perhaps the time series produced using the square root transformation might be more appropriately modelled by an additive model than that produced using the log transformation. However, the log transformation is more readily interpretable, so in practice, it might be best to try both and compare results.

Solution 4.1

(a) For a moving average of order 3, $q = 1$, so the moving average value for 1660 is

$$y_{1660} = \tfrac{1}{3}(x_{1659} + x_{1660} + x_{1661})$$
$$= \tfrac{1}{3}(8.83 + 9.08 + 9.75)$$
$$= 9.22.$$

Similarly, the moving average value for 1661 is 9.443, and that for 1662 is 9.277.

(b) To calculate the moving average value of order 3 for 1659 you would need the average temperature in 1658. However, the series given in Table 4.1 starts in 1659, so this value cannot be calculated. Similarly, to calculate the moving average value for 1663, you would need the average temperature for 1664, but this is not given in Table 4.1.

(c) Using the data from Table 4.1, a moving average of order 5 can be calculated only for 1661.

Solution 4.2

(a) The higher the order, the greater is the degree of smoothing. Hence Figure 4.5(a) was produced using a moving average of order 3. Figures 4.5(b), 4.5(c) and 4.5(d) were produced using moving averages of orders 11, 25 and 51, respectively.

(b) Figure 4.5(a) seems under-smoothed: much of the irregular variation in the original series is still present. Figure 4.5(d) seems over-smoothed: much of the detail has been lost and the smoothed series appears too flat. Figures 4.5(b) and 4.5(c) seem reasonable: which smooths by the right amount is to some extent a matter of opinion. Perhaps Figure 4.5(c) provides the better compromise between smoothing out the noise and smoothing out the trend. The best course of action would be to discuss with a chemist whether the peaks and troughs that appear in Figure 4.5(b) but not in Figure 4.5(c) might be important.

Solution 4.3

(a) First, the sum of the weights is 0.9, whereas for a weighted moving average the weights add up to 1. Secondly, the expression contains the term x_t^2, whereas only linear terms (such as x_t) are allowed.

(b) An appropriate weighted moving average of order 7 is

$$SA(t) = \tfrac{1}{6}(0.5x_{t-3} + x_{t-2} + x_{t-1} + x_t \\ + x_{t+1} + x_{t+2} + 0.5x_{t+3}).$$

Solution 4.4

(a) The trend appears to be downward between 1991 and 1993. After that, the trend is roughly level, before dipping between 1998 and 2000, then increasing again after 2001.

(b) The smoothed values, which are shown in Figure 4.9(b), are subtracted from the values in the original series (shown in Figure 4.9(a)) to produce a new series y_t. For each quarter, the raw seasonal factor is the average of the y_t for that quarter.

(c) The average of the raw seasonal factors is

$$\overline{F} = \tfrac{1}{4}(-2949.41 + 500.18 + 647.19 + 1760.50)$$
$$\simeq -10.39.$$

Thus the estimated seasonal factors are as follows:

$$\widehat{s}_1 = -2949.41 + 10.39 = -2939.02,$$
$$\widehat{s}_2 = 500.18 + 10.39 = 510.57,$$
$$\widehat{s}_3 = 647.19 + 10.39 = 657.58,$$
$$\widehat{s}_4 = 1760.50 + 10.39 = 1770.89.$$

(d) Beer consumption is highest in the fourth quarter (October–December), possibly because of high consumption leading up to and over Christmas. It is lowest in the first quarter (January–March).

Solution 4.5

(a) The seasonally adjusted time series appears to show a downward trend over the period. However, there is considerable noise, so it is difficult to visualize the trend.

(b) The trend estimate obtained with the moving average of order 3 is very jagged, suggesting that it is under-smoothed: not enough noise has been removed. The trend estimate obtained with the moving average of order 9 has removed the noise more successfully, without obscuring the detail. The moving average of order 9 is therefore preferable.

(c) The trend declines until the end of 1993, then rises slowly until 1997. It then drops again until 2001, after which it rises.

Solution 6.1

(a) The weights are shown in Table S.1.

Table S.1   Exponential weights

	c_0	c_1	c_2	c_3	c_4
$\alpha = 0.5$	0.5	0.25	0.125	0.0625	0.03125
$\alpha = 0.8$	0.8	0.16	0.032	0.0064	0.00128

(b) The weight given to the current observation is c_0, which is equal to α. Thus more weight is given to the current observation when $\alpha = 0.8$ than when $\alpha = 0.5$.

Solution 6.2

(a) Using expression (6.3),

$$\widehat{x}_{30} = \alpha x_{29} + (1 - \alpha)\widehat{x}_{29}$$
$$\simeq 0.6 \times 18.9 + (1 - 0.6) \times 20.263\,12$$
$$\simeq 19.445\,25,$$

$$\widehat{x}_{31} = \alpha x_{30} + (1 - \alpha)\widehat{x}_{30}$$
$$\simeq 0.6 \times 17.8 + (1 - 0.6) \times 19.445\,25$$
$$\simeq 18.458\,10,$$

$$\widehat{x}_{32} = \alpha x_{31} + (1 - \alpha)\widehat{x}_{31}$$
$$\simeq 0.6 \times 19.4 + (1 - 0.6) \times 18.458\,10$$
$$\simeq 19.023\,24.$$

(b) The 1-step ahead forecast of the temperature on 15 August, using data up to and including 14 August, is $\widehat{x}_{32}$. Rounded to one decimal place, this is $19.0°C$. The actual average temperature on 15 August was $18.9°C$.

Solution 6.3

(a) The optimal choice for α is the value which minimizes the SSE. The SSE is smallest for $\alpha = 0.05$, so the optimal value is 0.05. The corresponding forecast for the 2005 precipitation is 944.5 mm.

(b) The optimal value of α is very low. This means that little weight is placed on the most recent observations.

Solution 7.1

(a) The time series shows a very pronounced linear trend. The simple exponential smoothing method assumes there is no change in level, so it is not appropriate.

(b) A suitable initial value for the level is the first value of the series: $x_1 = 10.830\,13$. A suitable initial value for the slope is the difference between the first two values: $x_2 - x_1 = 10.844\,58 - 10.830\,13 = 0.014\,45$. This is a better choice than 0 in this case because of the pronounced trend in the time series.

(c) The optimal parameter combination is the one that minimizes the SSE. Hence the optimal combination is $\alpha = 1$ and $\gamma = 0.3$. The corresponding forecast is 11.9294, so the forecasted average house price (in pounds sterling) is $\exp(11.9294) \simeq 151\,700$.

(d) The forecast for August 2004 was too high, as it was based on an extrapolation of the trend. Subsequent forecasts gradually adjusted to the change in the trend.

Solution 7.2

(a) From Figure 7.8(b), the Holt–Winters forecasts track the seasonal variation more closely than the forecasts obtained using the other methods. Therefore the SSE for the Holt–Winters method is 799, the lowest of the three values. The SSE for Holt's method is 3300, and that for simple exponential smoothing is 3387. The smallest SSE is obtained with the Holt–Winters method because this method allows for seasonality, which is very marked in this time series. Holt's method is more flexible than simple exponential smoothing, in that it allows for a trend, so its SSE is (marginally) lower than that obtained using simple exponential smoothing.

(b) The Holt–Winters method is more appropriate for these data than the other two methods, and it produces a lower SSE. Hence the forecast from this method, namely $4.8°C$, is the most reliable.

Solution 7.3

(a) The forecast error for October 1987 is equal to the actual value minus the forecast for October 1987, that is, $1749.80 - 2406.94 = -657.14$. In previous months, the forecast errors were much smaller. Thus the forecast for October 1987 is very inaccurate.

(b) Using the Holt–Winters method might have improved the forecasts up to and including September 1987. But it would not have had a major impact on the forecast for October 1987, because seasonality does not account for the big drop.

Solution 9.1

(a) The time series lagged by 5 places is: *, *, *, *, *, 5, 1, 4, −9, 3.

(b) The sample autocorrelation r_3 is calculated using the pairs $(5, -9)$, $(1, 3)$, $(4, -3)$, $(-9, 7)$, $(3, 0)$, $(-3, -1)$, $(7, 8)$.

The sample autocorrelation r_6 is calculated using the pairs $(5, 7)$, $(1, 0)$, $(4, -1)$, $(-9, 8)$.

(c) The autocorrelation at lag 0 is a correlation coefficient calculated using the pairs (x_1, x_1), (x_2, x_2), $\ldots$, (x_n, x_n). Since there is exact agreement between the two values in each pair (and hence the corresponding points on a scatterplot lie exactly on a straight line), the autocorrelation is 1.

Solution 9.2

(a) No lag stands out as having a particularly high (in absolute value) autocorrelation. There is no systematic pattern. A suitable one-sentence summary is as follows. The autocorrelations up to lag 20 are all close to zero, with no clear pattern.

(b) If a clear pattern had emerged, or if some autocorrelations were far from zero, this might have suggested ways in which the forecasts might be improved. As it is, it is not clear how the forecasts could be improved upon.

Solution 9.3

(a) There is no change in the level of the time series of forecast errors. The size of the fluctuations does not appear to change, so there is no evidence that the variance of the forecast errors is changing systematically over time. (The slightly higher level at the beginning of the series is due to the choice of initial value and may be ignored.)

(b) The significance bounds are
$$\pm 1.96/\sqrt{239} \simeq \pm 0.127.$$

(c) The sample autocorrelations at lags 16 and 18 just cross the significance bounds. However, none of the sample autocorrelations clearly exceeds the bounds, hence there is little evidence of any non-zero population autocorrelations at lags 1 to 20.

Solution 9.4

(a) The test provides strong evidence of autocorrelation at lags 1 to 20.

(b) The significance bounds are
$$\pm 1.96/\sqrt{252} \simeq \pm 0.123.$$

(c) The sample autocorrelations at lags 3, 8 and 14 only just cross the bounds. The only autocorrelation that clearly exceeds one of the bounds is at lag 1. Thus there is clear evidence of non-zero autocorrelation only at lag 1.

Solution 9.5

(a) The time plot in Figure 9.10(a) suggests that the forecast errors have roughly constant variance. There are two outliers corresponding to forecast errors greater than 1 in absolute value, but these do not invalidate the conclusion that the variance is constant. Both Figure 9.10(a) and Figure 9.10(b) show that the forecast errors are distributed roughly symmetrically around zero. The histogram in Figure 9.10(b) is unimodal and roughly symmetric; this suggests that the normality assumption is valid. Finally, the Ljung–Box test provides only weak evidence for any non-zero autocorrelations up to lag 20. Thus the assumptions on which the calculation of prediction intervals is based appear valid; that is, the time series of forecast errors may be assumed to be white noise.

(b) An approximate 95% prediction interval is (x_{n+1}^-, x_{n+1}^+), where

$$x_{n+1}^- = \widehat{x}_{n+1} - z\sqrt{\frac{SSE}{n}}$$

$$= 17.50 - 1.96\sqrt{\frac{19.89}{197}} \simeq 16.88,$$

$$x_{n+1}^+ = \widehat{x}_{n+1} + z\sqrt{\frac{SSE}{n}}$$

$$= 17.50 + 1.96\sqrt{\frac{19.89}{197}} \simeq 18.12.$$

(c) The forecasted concentration at 396 hours, based on observed concentrations at two-hourly intervals up to 394 hours, is 17.5, with 95% prediction interval $(16.9, 18.1)$.

Solution 9.6

(a) For a 99% prediction interval, the 0.995-quantile of $N(0, 1)$ is required, so $z = 2.576$. The approximate 99% prediction limits, x_{n+1}^- and x_{n+1}^+, are given by

$$x_{n+1}^- = \widehat{x}_{n+1} - z\sqrt{\frac{SSE}{n}}$$

$$= 8.490 - 2.576\sqrt{\frac{0.3737}{205}} \simeq 8.380,$$

$$x_{n+1}^+ = \widehat{x}_{n+1} + z\sqrt{\frac{SSE}{n}}$$

$$= 8.490 + 2.576\sqrt{\frac{0.3737}{205}} \simeq 8.600.$$

(b) A forecast and prediction interval on the original scale may be obtained by applying the exponential function to these values. The forecast is

$$\exp(8.490) \simeq 4866,$$

and the 99% prediction limits are

$$\exp(8.380) \simeq 4359, \quad \exp(8.600) \simeq 5432.$$

Thus the forecasted value of the FTSE100 index is 4866, with approximate 99% prediction interval $(4359, 5432)$. (The actual value for February 2005 was 4968.50. This is close to the forecasted value, and lies within the prediction interval.)

Solution 11.1

(a) The time plot in Figure 11.3(a) displays no obvious trend or seasonality, and the variance seems roughly constant. Thus there is no reason to believe that the time series is not stationary. The time plot in Figure 11.3(b) displays marked seasonality, so this time series is not stationary in mean. Hence the time series is not stationary.

(b) The time plot in Figure 11.3(b) was obtained from that shown in Figure 11.3(a) by adding a seasonal component.

(c) The main difference between the two correlograms is the large periodic variation in Figure 11.3(d), which is not present in Figure 11.3(c). This periodic variation is induced by the seasonal component: a large positive value at time t will tend to be followed by large positive values at times $t + 12$ and $t + 24$ (and also at times $t + 36$, $t + 48$, and so on) and lower values at times halfway through the seasonal cycle, such as $t + 6$, $t + 18$, ... This induces large positive autocorrelations at lags 12 and 24, and large negative autocorrelations at lags 6 and 18.

Solution 11.2

The first and second differences are shown in Table S.2. Note that there are two empty cells in the column of second differences.

Table S.2   First and second differences

Period	Index	First difference	Second difference
Quarter 1, 1990	89.3	—	—
Quarter 2, 1990	90.6	1.3	—
Quarter 3, 1990	89.1	−1.5	−2.8
Quarter 4, 1990	88.3	−0.8	0.7
Quarter 1, 1991	87.2	−1.1	−0.3
Quarter 2, 1991	86.2	−1.0	0.1

The first differences are calculated as described in Example 11.4. The second differences are calculated from the first differences in the same way. For example, the second difference for the third quarter of 1990 is

$$z_3 = y_3 - y_2$$

$$= (-1.5) - 1.3$$

$$= -2.8.$$

Solution 11.3

(a) From Figure 11.7, there is an initial increasing trend until the mid 1940s, then a drop, followed by a further increase. The size of the irregular fluctuations does not appear to change with the level. Taking first differences eliminates the trend in the original time series, as does taking second differences: both the first differences and the second differences are stationary in mean.

(b) First-order differencing is sufficient to induce approximate stationarity in mean.

(c) The time series represented in Figure 11.8(a) is stationary in mean and in variance. There is no reason to suppose that the autocorrelation structure varies with time, so it is reasonable to conclude that the series is stationary.

Solution 12.1

(a) The time plot does not display any trend over time, and you are told that it is non-seasonal. So it is stationary in mean. The size of the fluctuations does not vary systematically (the single big spike at $t = 12$ does not amount to systematic variation). So the time series is stationary in variance. Hence there is no evidence to suggest that the series is not stationary.

(b) There are two main features: the first two autocorrelations exceed the 95% significance bounds, and the autocorrelations tend to alternate in sign.

(c) If an AR(1) model were appropriate, then β would be negative, reflecting the alternating sign of the autocorrelations.

Solution 12.2

(a) This is not an autoregressive model: X_t depends on X_1 and X_2, but not directly on its immediate predecessors.

(b) This is an autoregressive model of order 3, with parameters $\beta_1 = 0.6$, $\beta_2 = -0.2$, $\beta_3 = -0.05$.

(c) This is not an autoregressive model, because it involves X_{t-1}^2.

(d) This is an autoregressive model of order 2, with parameters $\beta_1 = -0.6$, $\beta_2 = 0.1$.

Solution 12.3

The partial autocorrelation at lag 1 in Figure 12.8(a) is -0.4. The PACF is zero at lags greater than 1. So $p = 1$ and $\beta_1 = -0.4$.

In Figure 12.8(b), the partial autocorrelation at lag 2 is -0.6, and the PACF is zero at higher lags. So $p = 2$ and, since $\alpha_p = \beta_p$ for an AR(p) model, $\beta_2 = -0.6$.

Solution 12.4

The sample partial autocorrelation at lag 1 exceeds the significance bounds. The sample partial autocorrelations at other lags are much smaller, and lie within or close to the significance bounds. Thus it is reasonable to conclude that the partial autocorrelations are zero at lags greater than 1. Thus an AR(1) model might be appropriate.

Solution 13.1

(a) There is no systematic variation in the level of the series, or in the size of the fluctuations. Hence there is no reason to suggest that the time series is not stationary.

(b) The correlogram shows a single large value at lag 1, and the remaining sample autocorrelations all lie within or only just cross the significance bounds. Furthermore, the partial correlogram shows an alternating pattern which is within the significance bounds for larger lags. So the suggestion that an MA(1) model is appropriate is reasonable.

(c) The patterns in the sample ACF and the sample PACF correspond roughly to those shown in Figures 13.1(c) and 13.1(d). This suggests that the value of θ is negative.

Solution 13.2

(a) This is not a moving average model, as it involves $\sqrt{Z_{t-2}}$.

(b) This is a moving average model of order 2. The autocorrelation at lag 2 is given by Formula (13.3):
$$\rho_2 = \frac{-\theta_2}{1 + \theta_1^2 + \theta_2^2} = \frac{-0.2}{1 + 0.5^2 + 0.2^2} \simeq -0.155.$$

(c) This is not a moving average model, as the right-hand side includes X_{t-1}.

(d) This is a moving average model of order 1. The autocorrelation at lag 1 is given by Formula (13.1):
$$\rho_1 = \frac{-\theta_1}{1 + \theta_1^2} = \frac{-(-0.9)}{1 + (-0.9)^2} \simeq 0.497.$$

Solution 13.3

(a) There is no systematic change in level, so the series is stationary in mean. There is no systematic change in the size of fluctuations, so the series is stationary in variance. Therefore there is no reason to suggest that the series is not stationary.

(b) First, there is a single large (and negative) sample autocorrelation at lag 1, and thereafter the sample autocorrelations are much smaller, and mainly lie within the significance bounds. Secondly, the sample partial autocorrelations tail off in magnitude.

(c) The order to choose is 1, since the sample autocorrelation at lag 1 is large in magnitude and all the others are close to zero.

Solution 14.1

(a) ARMA$(2,1)$

(b) ARMA$(0,1)$

(c) ARMA$(3,1)$

Solution 14.2

(a) ARIMA$(0,2,1)$

(b) ARIMA$(2,2,0)$

(c) Since the white noise model is ARMA$(0,0)$, the model for the original series is ARIMA$(0,2,0)$.

Solution 14.3

(a) The time plot in Figure 14.4(a) indicates that the series is not stationary in mean. The first differences in Figure 14.4(b) are stationary both in mean and in variance. There is no reason to suspect that the first differences are not stationary. Thus further differencing is not necessary, so $d = 1$.

(b) The sample autocorrelations are close to zero after lag 1, whereas the sample partial autocorrelations tail off with increasing lag. So a moving average model of order 1 is a plausible choice.

The white noise is not very plausible since, at lag 1, both the sample autocorrelation and sample partial autocorrelation exceed the significance bounds. Autoregressive and mixed models are also not very plausible as the sample ACF does not gradually tail off to zero, but is close to zero after lag 1.

(c) $\text{ARIMA}(0, 1, 1)$.

Solution 14.4

(a) The sample ACF is not close to zero (for the first few lags). This rules out the white noise model. The sample ACF could be interpreted as tailing off to zero gradually. Since the sample PACF has two large values at lags 1 and 2, this might suggest an $\text{AR}(2)$ model. However, another interpretation is that the partial autocorrelations tend to alternate in a damped sinusoidal pattern, so perhaps a mixed $\text{ARMA}(p, q)$ model is appropriate. The sample ACF could also be interpreted as being zero after lag 4, in which case an $\text{MA}(4)$ model would be appropriate.

(b) For the $\text{AR}(2)$ model, $p + q = 2$. The $\text{ARMA}(p, q)$ model has $p + q$ parameters. For the $\text{MA}(4)$ model, $p + q = 4$. Thus, using the principle of parsimony, the two 'best' candidate models, both with $p + q = 2$, are the $\text{AR}(2)$ and $\text{ARMA}(1, 1)$ models.

(c) The original time series is stationary, so $d = 0$. In ARIMA notation, the two models identified in part (b) are therefore $\text{ARIMA}(2, 0, 0)$ and $\text{ARIMA}(1, 0, 1)$.

Solution 14.5

Figure 14.9(a) shows that the 1-step ahead forecasts (the fitted values) closely match the observed values. However, to check the model adequacy in more detail, the forecast errors should be examined.

Figure 14.9(b) shows that the variance of the forecast errors is constant, and that they are distributed around zero. Figure 14.9(c) shows that their distribution is plausibly normal. Finally, Figure 14.9(d) shows that the autocorrelations at lags 1 to 20 are all small and, with perhaps one exception, lie within the significance bounds. Since we might expect about 1 autocorrelation out of 20 to exceed the bounds by chance if the underlying autocorrelations are zero, the sample ACF does not suggest that the forecast errors are correlated. This is confirmed by the Ljung–Box test: the p value of 0.24 provides little evidence against the null hypothesis that the autocorrelations at lags 1 to 20 are zero.

In conclusion, the $\text{ARIMA}(0, 1, 1)$ model is adequate for these data.

Solutions to Exercises

Solution 1.1

(a) There is no seasonal component because the data represent annual averages.

(b) There has been an increase of about 1°C (from about 9.3 to about 10.3) in the annual average temperature over the period. This is consistent with an increasing trend.

(c) The irregular component is very marked: there is substantial variation from year to year. This makes it difficult to pick out a trend.

Solution 1.2

The pattern is similar for different years, suggesting that beer consumption varies seasonally. The seasonal plot indicates that beer consumption is highest in the fourth quarter (October to December) and lowest in the first quarter (January to March).

Solution 2.1

The seasonal variation does not appear to vary much in size with the level of the series. It is hard to tell from Figure 1.3 whether or not the irregular fluctuations vary in size with the level. Overall, there is little reason to reject the additive model.

Solution 2.2

(a) The time series of monthly sales shows marked seasonal fluctuations. The size of the seasonal variation increases with the level of the series. Hence an additive model is not suitable.

(b) For the log transformed series in Figure 2.11(a), the seasonal fluctuations appear to be roughly of the same size, whatever the level of the series. For the time series of square roots, the seasonal variation increases with the level of the series. Thus the square root transformation does not produce a series which may be modelled by an additive model, whereas the log transformation might.

Solution 4.1

(a) Since seasonality may be ignored, only the irregular variation need be considered. The transformation appears to have been successful: there is no suggestion that the fluctuations of the irregular component vary with the level of the series.

(b) The time series in Figure 4.15(a) is the smoothest of the three, so it must have been obtained using the moving average with the highest order, that is, order 19. Figure 4.15(b) is the most spiky, so it was obtained using the moving average of order 3. Figure 4.15(c) was obtained using the moving average of order 11.

(c) This needs to be assessed in relation to the original series in Figure 4.14. In Figure 4.15(a), most of the detail has been smoothed out: perhaps this series is over-smoothed. In Figure 4.15(b), some short-term fluctuations remain, so perhaps this series is under-smoothed. This leaves the series in Figure 4.15(c) as the best compromise. But perhaps this one is also a little over-smoothed: the small bumps have been flattened out quite a lot. A moving average of order 7, for example, might be better than a moving average of order 11. The 'best' choice depends to some extent on whether features such as the 'small bumps' referred to here are important, and this is not a purely statistical question.

Solution 4.2

(a) The time plot of the original series is dominated by marked seasonal variation. The seasonally adjusted series suggests that there is some variation in the level over the period, but there is no clear upward or downward trend.

(b) The seasonal factors were estimated as follows. First, the original series was smoothed using a weighted moving average of order 13 to remove the seasonal fluctuations. Then this smoothed series was subtracted from the original series. The monthly averages of the resulting series were calculated next. Finally, the mean of these averages was subtracted from each average. The resulting values are the estimated seasonal factors.

Temperatures in Recife are highest between December and March, and lowest between June and August. The hottest month is February, and the coldest is August.

(c) The only difference between the two time plots is in the vertical scales on which they are drawn. Thus the degree of smoothness is the same in the two plots. Any apparent differences in smoothness are due to the different scales used. This emphasizes the importance of using the same scale when comparing time plots. Figure 4.17(a) is drawn on the same scale as the original data; this is the better choice of scale.

(d) There is substantial year-to-year variation, but no clear upward or downward trend.

Solution 6.1

(a) The initial value is $\widehat{x}_1 = x_1 = 17.0$, and the smoothing parameter α is 0.2, so, using (6.3),

$$\widehat{x}_2 = \alpha x_1 + (1-\alpha)\widehat{x}_1$$
$$= 0.2 \times 17.0 + (1-0.2) \times 17.0$$
$$= 17.0.$$

Similarly,

$$\widehat{x}_3 = \alpha x_2 + (1-\alpha)\widehat{x}_2$$
$$= 0.2 \times 16.6 + (1-0.2) \times 17.0$$
$$= 16.92,$$

$$\widehat{x}_4 = \alpha x_3 + (1-\alpha)\widehat{x}_3$$
$$= 0.2 \times 16.3 + (1-0.2) \times 16.92$$
$$= 16.796,$$

$$\widehat{x}_5 = \alpha x_4 + (1-\alpha)\widehat{x}_4$$
$$= 0.2 \times 16.1 + (1-0.2) \times 16.796$$
$$= 16.6568.$$

Thus the forecasted concentration at 10 hours (which corresponds to time point 5) is approximately 16.66.

(b) The SSE is given by

$$\sum_{t=1}^{4}(x_t - \widehat{x}_t)^2 = (17.0 - 17.0)^2 + (16.6 - 17.0)^2$$
$$+ (16.3 - 16.92)^2 + (16.1 - 16.796)^2$$
$$= 0 + 0.16 + 0.3844 + 0.484\,416$$
$$= 1.028\,816.$$

Hence the SSE is 1.029 to three decimal places.

Solution 6.2

(a) The optimal value of α among the values listed in Table 6.6 is 0.3. This is the value that gives the lowest SSE — 19.89 in this case. The corresponding forecast is 17.50.

(b) The time series of forecasts will be less smooth with $\alpha = 0.8$ than with $\alpha = 0.3$, because the forecasts depend to a greater extent on recent observations for larger values of α.

Solution 7.1

The time series in Figure 7.11(a) has no clear linear trend or (visible) seasonality, so simple exponential smoothing is likely to be appropriate.

The time series in Figure 7.11(b) has a marked linear trend, so simple exponential smoothing is definitely not appropriate. The fluctuations do not appear to vary in size with the level, so the series can be described using an additive model. Hence Holt's exponential smoothing might be appropriate or, if there is seasonality (which is not clear), Holt–Winters exponential smoothing.

The time series in Figure 7.11(c) has both an increasing linear trend and a clear seasonal cycle. Hence neither simple exponential smoothing nor Holt's exponential smoothing are appropriate. The seasonal and irregular fluctuations do not vary in size with the level, so an additive model can be used. The appropriate method is Holt–Winters exponential smoothing.

The time series in Figure 7.11(d) has an increasing trend and seasonality. However, the seasonal fluctuations increase in size with the level, and hence an additive model is not appropriate. If a transformation can be found such that an additive model is appropriate for the transformed series, then the Holt–Winters method could be used.

Solution 9.1

(a) The significance bounds are
$$\pm 1.96/\sqrt{n} = \pm 1.96/\sqrt{109} \simeq \pm 0.188.$$
The sample autocorrelation at lag 12 is -0.244, so it lies outside these bounds. This provides evidence against the null hypothesis that $\rho_{12} = 0$.

(b) The p value of 0.148 indicates that there is little evidence against the null hypothesis that the autocorrelations at lags 1 to 20 are zero. So there is little evidence that any of the autocorrelations $\rho_1, \rho_2, \ldots, \rho_{20}$ are non-zero.

(c) The correlogram shows that a single sample autocorrelation lies outside the significance bounds. Under the null hypothesis that all autocorrelations at lags 1 to 20 are zero, about 5% of these 20 (that is, 1) might be expected to lie outside the bounds. This is what was observed, so the correlogram is consistent with the result of the test in part (b).

However, in practice it would be worth investigating the autocorrelation at lag 12 a little more before dismissing it as a chance effect; because, for monthly data, lag 12 is rather special: it corresponds to the seasonal period. It could be that the Holt–Winters method is not capturing the seasonal variation adequately, and hence that the method could be improved.

Solution 9.2

(a) From Figure 9.12(a), the forecast errors appear to be distributed around zero with constant variance, and from Figure 9.12(b) they appear to be approximately normally distributed. So the assumption that the forecast errors are normally distributed with mean zero and constant variance is reasonable.

(b) The 95% prediction limits for the logarithm of the average house price in February 2005 are given by

$$x_{110}^{-} = \widehat{x}_{110} - 1.96\sqrt{\frac{SSE}{n}}$$
$$= 11.937 - 1.96\sqrt{\frac{0.006\,21}{109}}$$
$$\simeq 11.922,$$

$$x_{110}^{-} = \widehat{x}_{110} + 1.96\sqrt{\frac{SSE}{n}}$$
$$= 11.937 + 1.96\sqrt{\frac{0.006\,21}{109}}$$
$$\simeq 11.952.$$

(c) On the original scale, the forecasted value (in pounds sterling) is $\exp(11.937) \simeq 152\,800$.

The 95% prediction limits are $\exp(11.922) \simeq 150\,500$ and $\exp(11.952) \simeq 155\,100$.

In summary, the forecasted average house price in February 2005, based on data from January 1996 to January 2005 and rounded to the nearest £100, is £152 800, with approximate 95% prediction interval $(150\,500, 155\,100)$.

In fact, the average house price for February 2005 was £152 879. So the forecast was quite accurate and certainly within the prediction interval.

Solution 11.1

The time series is (approximately) stationary in mean, because there is no systematic variation in the level of the time series, and you are told the time series is not seasonal. However, the time series is not stationary in variance, as the size of the irregular fluctuations suddenly increases shortly after time point 100.

Solution 11.2

The first differences are calculated as described in Example 11.4. The same method is then applied to the first differences to obtain the second differences. The first and second differences are shown in Table S.3.

Table S.3   First and second differences

Time	Value	First difference	Second difference
1	1790.8	–	–
2	1768.8	−22.0	–
3	1742.5	−26.3	−4.3
4	1802.2	59.7	86.0
5	1784.4	−17.8	−77.5
6	1857.6	73.2	91.0

Solution 12.1

(a) This model is autoregressive of order 2.

(b) This model is not autoregressive, as it involves the term $X_{t-1}X_{t-2}$.

(c) This model is autoregressive of order 1.

Solution 12.2

(a) The partial correlogram shows a large negative value at lag 1. All the other sample partial autocorrelations are close to zero, and lie within the significance bounds. Thus an AR(1) model would appear to be appropriate for these data.

(b) For an AR(1) model, $\alpha_1 = \beta_1$. The sample partial autocorrelation at lag 1 is roughly -0.6, so $\beta_1 \simeq -0.6$.

Solution 13.1

Time series 1: A moving average model of order 2 is appropriate, since the sample autocorrelations at lags 1 and 2 are the largest in magnitude and exceed the significance bounds, whereas all the others are close to zero and lie within the significance bounds. The sample PACF tails off to zero in magnitude with increasing lag.

Time series 2: A moving average model of order 3 is appropriate, since the sample autocorrelations at lags 1, 2 and 3 exceed the significance bounds, whereas all the others are close to zero and lie within the significance bounds. The sample PACF tails off to zero in magnitude with increasing lag.

Solution 14.1

In an ARIMA(p, d, q) model, p is the order of the autoregressive component of the model, d is the order of differencing, and q is the order of the moving average component. Hence the models given can be described as follows.

(a) ARIMA$(2, 2, 0)$

(b) ARIMA$(1, 0, 2)$

(c) ARIMA$(1, 1, 1)$

(d) ARIMA$(0, 1, 1)$

Solution 14.2

(a) After lag 2, the sample partial autocorrelations lie close to zero and do not exceed the significance bounds, so an autoregressive model with $p = 2$ might be appropriate.

(b) After lag 3, the sample autocorrelations lie close to zero and do not exceed the significance bounds, so a moving average model with $q = 3$ might be appropriate.

(c) An alternative interpretation of the correlogram and the partial correlogram is that both the sample ACF and the PACF tail off to zero with increasing lag. Therefore an ARMA$(1, 1)$ model might be appropriate.

(d) The value of $p + q$ is 2 for an AR(2) model, 3 for an MA(3) model, and 2 for an ARMA$(1, 1)$ model. According to the principle of parsimony, the shortlist of models should include the AR(2) model and the ARMA$(1, 1)$ model.

Solution 14.3

The histogram suggests that the forecast errors may well be normally distributed. However, the correlogram suggests that the forecast errors are not uncorrelated: there is a large positive autocorrelation at lag 2. This is confirmed by the Ljung–Box test: the p value of 0.01 provides strong evidence against the null hypothesis that the autocorrelations at lags 1 to 20 are zero. Therefore it can be concluded that an MA(1) model is not adequate.

Solution 16.1

This exercise covers some of the ideas and techniques discussed in Sections 1 and 2.

(a) The time series is cyclical. There does not appear to be a trend: the level of the series fluctuates around a mean value that does not change over time. The irregular fluctuations appear to be larger at the tops of the cyclical peaks than in the troughs. Over the 50-year period spanned by these data, there were four complete cycles and most of a fifth cycle. So the period T is a little over ten years.

(b) An additive model would not be appropriate, because the size of the irregular fluctuations is greater at the tops of the peaks than in the troughs.

(c) The log transformation is not appropriate because the size of the irregular fluctuations in Figure 16.2(a) is greater in the troughs than at the peaks. The square root transformation may be appropriate: the size of the irregular fluctuations in Figure 16.2(b) seems to be similar at all points of the cycle.

Solution 16.2

This exercise covers some of the ideas and techniques discussed in Sections 1 and 4.

(a) The main feature of the plot is the strong seasonality, which dominates the plot. No trend is discernible, because of the strong seasonality. The maximum temperatures in cold months appear to be more variable than the maximum temperatures in warm months, since the lower edge of the plot is more ragged than the upper edge.

(b) The seasonal factors are estimated as follows. First, the time series is smoothed using the following weighted moving average:
$$SA(t) = \tfrac{1}{12}(0.5X_{t-6} + X_{t-5} + \cdots + X_t$$
$$+ \cdots + X_{t+5} + 0.5X_{t+6}).$$
The values obtained are subtracted from the values in the original series, and the raw seasonal factors F_j are obtained by calculating the monthly averages of these differences.

Next, the average $\overline{F}$ of the F_j is calculated.

Then the seasonal factors are estimated as
$$\widehat{s}_j = F_j - \overline{F}.$$
The estimated seasonal factors show that the maximum monthly temperatures are highest in July and lowest in January.

(c) The higher the order of the moving average that is used, the greater is the smoothing produced. Thus Figure 16.4(a) corresponds to the seasonally adjusted series, Figure 16.4(b) to the moving average of order 51, Figure 16.4(c) to the moving average of order 11, and Figure 16.4(d) to the moving average of order 121.

(d) The moving average of order 11 results in a plot which appears under-smoothed: there is still much irregular fluctuation. The moving average of order 121 produces a plot which is perhaps a little over-smoothed. So the moving average of order 51 is a reasonable compromise. However, note that this choice is to a large extent subjective: for example, it would be quite reasonable to choose Figure 16.4(d) if you believed that the irregularities in Figure 16.4(b) were due to noise.

(e) The level appears broadly constant until about 1970. During the 1970s there appears to be some fluctuation. After 1980 the level is again roughly constant, though perhaps slightly higher than before 1970.

Solution 16.3

This exercise covers some of the ideas and techniques discussed in Section 6.

(a) The time plot shows an increasing trend between 1988 and 2000. Between 2000 and 2005, the time series does not show a clear trend. The irregular fluctuations appear not to vary in size as the level of the series changes. Hence an additive model is appropriate for this time series.

(b) Since there is no seasonal variation (as stated in the question), the Holt–Winters method is not needed. Since the data from 2000 are to be used, and there is no clear trend during that period, simple exponential smoothing is probably the best method to use.

(c) The starting value is the first value of the series, namely $x_1 = \log(10\,940.53) \simeq 9.3002$.

(d) The optimal value of the parameter α is the value that minimizes the SSE, so $\alpha = 0.9$. This is a high value, indicating that forecasts depend largely on the most recent observations.

(e) The 1-step ahead forecast of the logarithm of the Dow Jones index for July 2005 is given by
$$\widehat{x}_{\text{July 2005}} = \alpha\,x_{\text{June 2005}} + (1 - \alpha)\,\widehat{x}_{\text{June 2005}}$$
$$= 0.9 \times 9.2375 + (1 - 0.9) \times 9.2537$$
$$\simeq 9.2391.$$

A forecast for the index on the original scale is obtained by applying the exponential function to this value. Thus the forecasted value of the Dow Jones index for July 2005 is $\exp(9.2391) \simeq 10\,292$.

Solution 16.4

This exercise covers some of the ideas and techniques discussed in Sections 7 and 9.

(a) The time plot suggests that the forecast errors are distributed with mean zero and constant variance. (A possible exception is at the start of the series, where the errors tend to be negative. This is due to the choice of starting values, and may be ignored.) The histogram suggests that the distribution is normal. Thus it is reasonable to assume that the forecast errors are distributed normally with mean zero and constant variance.

(b) The 95% significance bounds are

$$\pm 1.96/\sqrt{n} = \pm 1.96/\sqrt{210} \simeq \pm 0.135.$$

None of the sample correlations at lags 1 to 20 exceeds the significance bounds, so there is little evidence to suggest that the underlying autocorrelations are non-zero.

A time series is white noise if it is normal with mean zero and constant variance, and all autocorrelations at lags $k \geq 1$ are zero. From the results above and those obtained in part (a), there is no compelling reason to believe that this is not the case.

(c) The 95% prediction limits for the July 2005 value of the log Dow Jones index are given by

$$x^- = \widehat{x} - 1.96\sqrt{\frac{SSE}{n}}$$

$$= 9.2407 - 1.96\sqrt{\frac{0.3925}{210}} \simeq 9.1560,$$

$$x^+ = \widehat{x} + 1.96\sqrt{\frac{SSE}{n}}$$

$$= 9.2407 + 1.96\sqrt{\frac{0.3925}{210}} \simeq 9.3254.$$

The forecast for the Dow Jones index is obtained by applying the exponential function to this forecast and to these prediction limits:

$$\exp(9.2407) \simeq 10\,308,$$
$$\exp(9.1560) \simeq 9471,$$
$$\exp(9.3254) \simeq 11\,219.$$

Thus the forecast for the July 2005 value of the Dow Jones index is $10\,308$, with 95% prediction interval $(9471, 11\,219)$.

Solution 16.5

This exercise covers some of the ideas and techniques discussed in Sections 11 to 14.

(a) There is no systematic change in the level of the time series (and you are told that the series is not seasonal), so the time series is stationary in mean. However, the magnitude of the irregular fluctuations increases over time, so the series is not stationary in variance. Hence the series is not stationary.

(b) The time plot in Figure 16.5 shows that the time series of logarithms of the Dow Jones index is not stationary in mean. The time plots in Figure 16.9 suggest that both the first and the second differences are stationary in mean and in variance. Hence neither offers any evidence of non-stationarity. The order of differencing is the smallest number of differences required to obtain a stationary series, so $d = 1$.

(c) None of the sample autocorrelations and sample partial autocorrelations at lags 1 to 20 exceeds the 95% significance bounds. Thus there is little evidence that the underlying autocorrelations and partial autocorrelations at lags 1 to 20 are non-zero.

(d) From part (c), a plausible model for the time series of first differences is the white noise model. Since $d = 1$, the model for the logarithms of the Dow Jones index is ARIMA$(0, 1, 0)$.

Solution 16.6

This exercise covers some of the ideas and techniques discussed in Sections 11 to 14.

(a) The sample autocorrelation function declines gradually, whereas the sample partial autocorrelation function appears to drop close to zero after lag 2. This would suggest that an AR(2) model is appropriate. Since no differencing is involved, this corresponds to an ARIMA$(2, 0, 0)$ model.

Other interpretations are possible, though perhaps they are less plausible. For example, the sample partial autocorrelations could be deemed to decline gradually as well as the sample autocorrelations. This suggests an ARIMA$(p, 0, q)$ model with both p and q greater than zero. Applying the principle of parsimony then leads to the ARIMA$(1, 0, 1)$ model, for which $p + q = 2$, the same as for the ARIMA$(2, 0, 0)$ model.

(b) The correlogram cuts off abruptly after lag 1, while the sample partial autocorrelations decline gradually in absolute value. This is typical of an MA(1) model. Since the series has been differenced once, $d = 1$. Thus an ARIMA$(0, 1, 1)$ model is reasonable.

(c) The model formula for the first differences Y_t is

$$Y_t - 0.007 = Z_t - 0.865 Z_{t-1},$$

where Z_t is white noise with standard deviation 4.042.

(d) The p value of 0.003 for the ARIMA$(0, 1, 1)$ model provides strong evidence against the null hypothesis that the forecast errors are uncorrelated at lags 1 to 20. Thus the ARIMA$(0, 1, 1)$ is not adequate.

The p value of 0.541 for the ARIMA$(2, 0, 0)$ model provides little evidence against the null hypothesis of zero correlation of the forecast errors at lags 1 to 20. To decide whether the ARIMA$(2, 0, 0)$ model is adequate, it is necessary to check that the distribution of the forecast errors is normal with mean zero and constant variance. This can be done by examining the time plot and a histogram of the forecast errors.

Index